Student Note-Taking Guide to Accompany

Legal and Ethical Issues

for Health Professionals

George D. Pozgar, MBA, CHE
Consultant and Hospital Surveyor
Gp Healthcare Consulting, Int'l.
Annapolis, Maryland

Legal Review
Nina M. Santucci, JD
General Counsel
Annapolis, Maryland

JONES AND BARTLETT PUBLISHERS
Sudbury, Massachusetts
BOSTON   TORONTO   LONDON   SINGAPORE

World Headquarters
Jones and Bartlett Publishers
40 Tall Pine Drive
Sudbury, MA 01776
978-443-5000
info@jbpub.com
www.jbpub.com

Jones and Bartlett Publishers
Canada
6339 Ormindale Way
Mississauga, Ontario
L5V 1J2
CANADA

Jones and Bartlett Publishers
International
Barb House, Barb Mews
London W6 7PA
UK

Jones and Bartlett's books and products are available through most bookstores and online booksellers. To contact Jones and Bartlett Publishers directly, call 800-832-0034, fax 978-443-8000, or visit our website www.jbpub.com.

Substantial discounts on bulk quantities of Jones and Bartlett's publications are available to corporations, professional associations, and other qualified organizations. For details and specific discount information, contact the special sales department at Jones and Bartlett via the above contact information or send an email to specialsales@jbpub.com.

6048

Production Credits
Executive Editor: David Cella
Production Director: Amy Rose
Associate Production Editor: Rachel Rossi
Editorial Assistant: Lisa Gordon
Associate Marketing Manager: Jennifer Bengtson
Manufacturing Buyer: Amy Bacus
Printing and Binding: Courier-Stoughton.
Cover Printing: Courier-Stoughton

Printed in the United States of America
10 09 08 07 06   10 9 8 7 6 5 4 3 2 1

Contents

How This Book Can Help You Learn

All of us have different learning styles. Some of us are visual learners, some more auditory, some learn better by doing an activity. Some students prefer to learn new material using visual aids. Some learn material better when they hear it in a lecture; others learn it better by reading it. Cognitive research has shown that no matter what your learning style, you will learn more if you are actively engaged in the learning process.

This Student Note-Taking Guide will help you learn by providing a structure to your notes and letting you utilize all of the learning styles mentioned above. Students don't need to copy down every word their professor says or recopy their entire textbook. Do the assigned reading, listen in lecture, follow the key points your instructor is making, and write down meaningful notes. After reading and lectures, review your notes and pull out the most important points.

The Student Note-Taking Guide is your partner and guide in note-taking. Your Guide provides you with a visual guide that follows the chapter topics presented in your textbook. If your instructor is using the PowerPoint slides that accompany the text, this guide will save you from having to write down everything that is on the slides. There is space provided for you to jot down the terms and concepts that you feel are most important to each lecture. By working with your Guide, you are seeing, hearing, writing, and, later, reading and reviewing. The more often you are exposed to the material, the better you will learn and understand it. Using different methods of exposure significantly increases your comprehension.

Your Guide is the perfect place to write down questions that you want to ask your professor later, interesting ideas that you want to discuss with your study group, or reminders to yourself to go back and study a certain concept again to make sure that you really got it.

Having organized notes is essential at exam time and when doing homework assignments. Your ability to easily locate the important concepts of a recent lecture will help you move along more rapidly, as you don't have to spend time rereading an entire chapter just to reinforce one point that you may not have quite understood.

Your Guide is a valuable resource. You've found a wonderful study partner!

Note-Taking Tips

1. It is easier to take notes if you are not hearing the information for the first time. Read the chapter or the material that is about to be discussed before class. This will help you to anticipate what will be said in class, and have an idea of what to write down. It will also help to read over your notes from the last class. This way you can avoid having to spend the first few minutes of class trying to remember where you left off last time.

2. Don't waste your time trying to write down everything that your professor says. Instead, listen closely and only write down the important points. Review these important points after class to help remind you of related points that were made during the lecture.

3. If the class discussion takes a spontaneous turn, pay attention and participate in the discussion. Only take notes on the conclusions that are relevant to the lecture.

4. Emphasize main points in your notes. You may want to use a highlighter, special notation (asterisks, exclamation points), format (circle, underline), or placement on the page (indented, bulleted). You will find that when you try to recall these points, you will be able to actually picture them on the page.

5. Be sure to copy down word-for-word specific formulas, laws, and theories.

6. Hearing something repeated, stressed, or summed up can be a signal that it is an important concept to understand.

7. Organize handouts, study guides, and exams in your notebook along with your lecture notes. It may be helpful to use a three-ring binder, so that you can insert pages wherever you need to.

8. When taking notes, you might find it helpful to leave a wide margin on all four sides of the page. Doing this allows you to note names, dates, definitions, etc., for easy access and studying later. It may also be helpful to make notes of questions you want to ask your professor about or research later, ideas or relationships that you want to explore more on your own, or concepts that you don't fully understand.

9. It is best to maintain a separate notebook for each class. Labeling and dating your notes can be helpful when you need to look up information from previous lectures.

10. Make your notes legible, and take notes directly in your notebook. Chances are you won't recopy them no matter how noble your intentions. Spend the time you would have spent recopying the notes studying them instead, drawing conclusions and making connections that you didn't have time for in class.

11. Look over your notes after class while the lecture is still fresh in your mind. Fix illegible items and clarify anything you don't understand. Do this again right before the next class.

Notes

Student Study Guide

Fundamental Questions of Law and Ethics – I

The fundamental questions of law and ethics include, "What should I do?" or "How should I act?" Because the answers are not always clear, the text, **_Legal and Ethical Issues for Health Care Professionals_** and this **_Student Study Guide_** have been designed to help the reader to make good decisions in difficult situations.

Fundamental Questions of Law and Ethics – II

- Health care professionals are constantly bombarded by a variety of legal & ethical issues on a daily basis. This guide may be the caregiver's only exposure to the law & ethics. It is critical for the student to learn:
  - how our own values effect our decisions,
  - how to examine a dilemma from the perspective opposite of the one we hold, &
  - how our values & decisions may change through this process.

The Law & Ethics

- This text includes an introduction to law & the application of ethical theories, principles, virtues, & values.
- The resolution of ethical dilemmas is like a never ending story with never ending questions.
- At some point questions must cease & critical decisions made, often involving the quality of life (e.g., when to hold on & when to let go).

More Questions than Answers

Naval Cadets had to make some difficult decisions after taking their ethics course at the Naval Academy.

U.S. Naval Academy

"This course, Ethics and Moral Reasoning . . . Requires midshipman to answer questions about who will live and who will die — questions so tough that a number of these students may choose not to return next year, according to juniors who took this course last year."

The Capital, Annapolis, Maryland October 9, 2006

Note –Taking Tips

- Read & review the assigned chapter, study guide, class notes, & other assigned readings prior to class.
- Make note of important points.
- Review class notes after class lectures.
- Record other facts you may recall.
- Abbreviate frequently used words.
- healthy food + adequate sleep + exercise = a healthy, open mind, ready to learn!

Case Reviews – I

- Discuss cases in the context of:
  - Class lectures
  - Textbook
  - Other assigned readings
  - Life experiences

Case Reviews – II

- Describe the legal aspects of the case.
- When given, do you agree with the court's decision? Explain your answer.
- Describe the ethical issues of the case.
- Describe how one's professional code of ethics applies.

Notes

Notes

Case Reviews – III

- Discuss how ethical dilemmas impact family members, physicians, other caregivers.
- Discuss how your relationship with the patient (e.g., friend, family, stranger) may affect your ability to offer an objective opinion.

Case Reviews – IV

- Describe how one's own values, beliefs, religion, education, & life experiences impact decisions.
- Describe how financial concerns can affect the decision-making process.
- Describe how corporate culture can affect the decision-making process (e.g., elective abortions in a catholic hospital).

Premises & Conclusions – I

- In a logical argument, our premises limit conclusions derived from them. **If** premises X1 & X2 are accurate & true and not contradictory **then** a conclusion drawn from them may be true.
- However, **if** X1 & X2 are not accurate and contradictory **then** a conclusion may be invalid, for example:

Premises & Conclusions – II

X1 Doe is pro-life.
X2 Doe would not vote for a pro-choice politician
Y   Therefore, Doe is a good person.

Conclusion?

Doe is a good person because he is pro-life & would not vote for a pro-choice politician. Do you agree with the conclusion that Doe is a good person?

Premises and Conclusions – III

- Doe may be considered a good person by some in this instance; however, you cannot judge Doe's total moral character as being good merely because he is pro-life.
- Reasoning: Doe may seek to injure those who are pro-choice.

The Court Room Setting

- The judge decides questions of law.
- The jury is the finder of facts.
- The plaintiff accuses the defendant of wrong doing and the plaintiff's attorney argues his case.
- The defendant is the one accused of wrongdoing and the defendant's attorney defends the defendant.

Notes

Notes

The Ethics Committee Setting

Think of the courtroom setting as a place where the ethics committee meets.

- The judge is the committee chairman.
- The jury represents the members of the ethics committee.
- Think of the plaintiff as the patient, the plaintiff's attorney as the patient's advocate (e.g., the patient's surrogate decision-maker).
- The defendant as an adversarial advocate (e.g., disgruntled family member), and the defendant's attorney as legal counsel for an adversarial advocate.

Conducting Consultations – I

- Ethics consultations may be called to
  - clarify ethical issues
  - facilitate discussion of an ethical dilemma
  - resolve an ethical dispute.

Conducting Consultations – II

- The consultation mechanism may be through
  - an ethics committee
  - a subset of the committee
  - individual consultants
  - consultation teams

Conducting Consultations – III

- Ethics consultations are used to assist the patient & family in making difficult treatment decisions (e.g., withdrawing of life support systems).
- Caregivers, patient, & family may request an ethics consultation.
- Caregivers, patient, & family members may attend consultations.

Conducting Consultations – IV

- All persons are treated with respect for their individual beliefs.
- Judgments based on one's personal beliefs & biases must be avoided.

Ethical Dilemmas
Decision Making Process - I

1. Identify the problem.
2. Identify legal & ethical issues.
3. Review relevant legal & ethical resources.
4. Apply ethical & legal principles.
5. Consider alternative courses of action.

Notes

_____
_____
_____
_____
_____
_____
_____
_____
_____
_____
_____
_____
_____
_____
_____
_____
_____
_____
_____
_____
_____
_____
_____
_____
_____
_____
_____
_____
_____
_____
_____
_____
_____
_____
_____

Ethical Dilemmas
Decision Making Process - II

1. List the pros & cons of each course of action.
2. Know when to seek expert help (clergy, lawyer, ethicist, physician).
3. Decide on a preferred best course of action.
4. Advise, where applicable, patient, surrogate decision-maker, family, caregivers.

Time- Is the Enemy

- Make your best decision based on facts.
- Accept the fact that you will <u>Never</u> have answers to all the questions.
- Review the following cases by discussing the legal and ethical issues involved.
  - NOTE: The student is not provided all possible legal & ethical issues that may be present in a particular case. Issues presented are merely a beginning point for case discussion.

Case 1: Misdiagnosis

Mr. Jones arrived in the ER complaining of minor chest pains & numbness in his right arm. Jones is an undocumented alien and has no insurance. Mr. Jones believes he had strained his left arm playing ball with some friends earlier that day. After the game Mr. Jones and a few of his fellow players had lunch at the Fishy Spoon restaurant where he had a tuna fish sandwich, which he thought had a strange taste. Following a brief examination, the physician sent Mr. Jones home suggesting that he take some TUMS®. Mr. Jones passed away in his sleep during the night.

Case 1: Legal Issues

- Mistakes become negligence when the following elements of are proven:
  1. Duty to Care
  2. Breach of Duty
  3. Injury
  4. Causation
     a. Foreseeability

Case 1: Legal Issues-Negligence

1. Duty to Care
 – The hospital had a duty to care for Mr. Jones.

2. Breach of Duty
 – Based on the evidence presented, the jury determined that the ED physician did not perform an adequate examination based on the patient's complaints.

Case 1: Legal Issues-Negligence

3. Injury
 – Mr. Jones died of an MI.

4. Causation
 – The jury determined it was <u>foreseeable</u> that the cursory examination in light of Mr. Jones's symptoms led to inappropriate treatment & his untimely death. Mr. Jones may have died anyway. But he was denied his opportunity for life & thus this negligence case and the jury's finding for the plaintiff – Mr. Jones.

Case 1: Ethical Issues

- Justice
  - Treat all equally
    - Do you think the patient's ability to pay affected the level of treatment?

Case 2: Dad is OK

I was visiting with dad & observed that he was experiencing severe difficulty breathing. He reluctantly allowed me to take him to the hospital ED. He was examined by the ED physician, who had ordered chest x-rays. A few hours later the ED physician came to me in the waiting area & said the chest x-rays showed that dad had emphysema. He then went on to say that it is people like my dad who tie up the emergency room delaying treatment for more serious patients. Happy to hear my dad would be OK, I ignored the physician's comments.

Case 2: Ethical Issues

- Compassion
- Fairness
- Kindness
- Respect

Case 2: Dad is Not OK!

Dad received a telephone call the next day from the hospital. He was told that he had a suspicious spot on his lung. He was asked to follow-up with his family physician. Dad was diagnosed with lung cancer.

Case 2: Legal Issues-Negligence?

- The element of *injury* could not be established as a result of the one day delay in dad's treatment.
  - Therefore negligence cannot be established.
- Had there been no notification to dad as to the spot on his lung & his life shortened, there would be grounds for a lawsuit.

No New Patients Accepted

Most primary care physicians at Boston's top hospitals are so busy that they have officially closed their practices to new patients. Exceptions for family members, patients, & colleagues are accepted as a favor.

Boston Sunday Globe, November 12, 2006.

Discuss the ethical issues of this practice?

Notes

_____

_____

_____

_____

_____

_____

_____

_____

_____

_____

_____

_____

_____

_____

_____

_____

_____

_____

_____

_____

_____

_____

_____

_____

_____

_____

_____

_____

_____

_____

_____

_____

_____

_____

_____

_____

_____

_____

_____

_____

_____

_____

_____

_____

_____

_____

_____

_____

_____

_____

Patient Dumping

Prosecutors filed criminal charges against a major hospital accusing it of dumping a homeless patient suffering from dementia on the city's crime-plagued Skid Row. General Hospital is among 10 under investigation for allegedly discharging homeless patients onto the streets instead of into the custody of a relative or shelter.

Discuss the legal & ethical issues of this scenario.

Notes

Chapter 1
Introduction to Ethics

Any Good I Can Do

I expect to pass through the world but once. Any good therefore that I can do, or any kindness I can show to any creature, let me do it now. Let me not defer it, for I shall not pass this way again.

Stephen Grellet, French/American religious leader (1773-1855).

Learning Objectives - I

- Understand relevant "ethical theories"
- Describe "ethical principles"
- Understand concepts of morality, virtues, & values.
- Understand concept of situational ethics.

Notes

_____

Learning Objectives - II

- Provide a foundation to help in understanding ethical dilemmas.
- Learn how to determine the rightness & wrongness of alternative courses of action.
- Understand how ethical dilemmas occur when values, rights, duties, & loyalties conflict.

Ethics Defined - I

- Branch of philosophy
- Study of morals & character
- Study of principles of human dignity
- Ethics provide us with "moral principles" or universal rules that us know what to do.

Ethics Defined - II

- Involves how individuals decide to live
  - within accepted & desirable principles
  - in harmony with the environment & one another
- *Micro-ethics*: individual's view of right & wrong
- *Macro-ethics*: global view of right & wrong

Focus of Health Care Ethics

- Values relating to human conduct.
- Rightness & wrongness of actions.
- Goodness & badness of motives & ends
- Provide the tools for constructive deliberation & conflict resolution involving ethical dilemmas.

MILESTONES - I

- 1932–72 - Tuskegee Study of Syphilis
- 1946 - Military Tribunal for War Crimes
- 1949 - Nuremberg Trials
  - Int'l Code of Medical Ethics
- 1954 - First Kidney transplant
- 1960s - Cardio-pulmonary resuscitation

MILESTONES - II

- 1968 - Harvard Medical School
  - report on Brain Death Criteria
- 1964 - World Medical Association
- 1970 - Patient as a Person
  - by Paul Ramsey
  - "paternalism" questioned
- 1971 - Kennedy Institute of Ethics at Georgetown

Notes

Notes

MILESTONES - III

- 1972 - Informed Consent
- 1974 - National Research Act
- 1976 - Substituted Judgment
  – *In the Matter of Karen Ann Quinlan*
- 1978 - President's Commission for Study of Ethical Problems in Medicine

MILESTONES - IV

- 1990 - Physician Assisted Suicide
- 1990 - Patient Self-Determination Act
- 1994 - Oregon's Death with Dignity Act
- 1996 - HIPAA

MILESTONES - V

- 2001 - President's Council on Bioethics
- 2003 - Human Genome Fully Sequenced
- 2006 - Stem Cell Research Controversy

Theory: Normative Ethics – I

- Determining what moral standards should be followed
- General normative ethics
  - Determining correct moral principles

Theory: Normative Ethics – II

- Applied ethics
  - Application of normative theories to practical moral problems, for example,
    - Abortion
    - Euthanasia
    - Physician assisted suicide
    - Stem Cell Research

Theory: Consequential Ethics

- The morally right action involves
  - maximum balance of good or evil
- Utilitarianism
  - form of consequentialism
  - philosophy that advocates the greatest good for the greatest number
  - everyone is obligated to do whatever will achieve the greatest good for the greatest number.

Notes

Theory: Non-Consequential Ethics

- Rightness or wrongness of an action is based on properties intrinsic to the action.
  - not on its consequences

Theory: Deontological Ethics

- Focuses on duty to others
- *Forms*
  - *Religious Ethics*
    - *based on religious beliefs*
  - *Secular Ethics*
    - *based on codes developed by societies that have relied on customs*

Principles of Health Care Ethics

- Autonomy
  - right to make one's own decisions
- Beneficence
  - principle of doing good
- Nonmaleficence
  - avoid causing harm
- Justice
  - obligation to be fair

Age & Justice - I

- Should an 89 year old patient get a heart transplant because he or she is higher on the waiting list to receive a heart transplant than a ten year old girl?

Age & Justice - II

- Should a pregnant 39 year old single parent get a heart transplant because he or she is higher on the waiting list to receive a heart transplant than a ten year old boy?

Which Disaster Patients Get Treated First?

- Room #1: Severely injured patients not expected to live.

- Room #2: Severely injured patients most likely to live if treated.

- Room #3: Injured patients will live but will suffer varying degrees of disability if not treated promptly.

Notes

Notes

Emergency Care

Two patients in critical condition, who gets treated first:

- 1st patient who walks through door
- younger patient
- patient most likely to survive
- patient who can pay for services
- patient with most serious condition

Scarce Resources

- What happens when resources are scarce & only one of two patients can be treated?
- What should be the determining factors
  - age
  - position in life
  - patient wishes . . .

Morality

- Is a code of conduct.
- Implies quality of being in accord with standards of right & good conduct.
- Describes class of rules held by society to govern the conduct of its individual members.

Morals

- Ideas about what is right & wrong.
- Guides to behavior that rational persons put forward for governing their behavior.

Moral Responsibility

- Requires a person to question his or her own values.
- Requires a person not only to examine what one considers right thing to do in given situation, but why it is the right thing to do.
- A *moral dilemma* occurs when moral ideas of right & wrong conflict.

Moral Judgments - I

- Judgments concerned with what an individual or group believes to be right or proper behavior in a given situation.
- Involves assessment of another person's moral character based on how he or she conforms to moral convictions established by the individual &/or group.
- Lack of conformity typically results in:
  - moral censure
  - condemnation
  - possibly derision of the violator's character

Notes

Moral Judgments - II

- What is considered right varies from nation to nation, culture to culture, religion to religion, & person to person.
- No "universal morality."
- Whatever guide to behavior an individual regards as overriding & wants to be universally adopted is considered that individual's morality.

Morality Legislated

- Law is distinguished from morality in that
  - the law has explicit rules, penalties, & officials who interpret the laws & apply the penalties.
- Laws are created to set boundaries for societal behaviour.
  - laws are enforced to ensure that expected behavior happens

Virtues - I
Approach to Normative Ethics

- Attitudes, dispositions, or character traits that enable us to be and to act in ways that develop this potential.
- Character traits valued as being good
  - differentiate good people from bad people
  - guides to our actions
  - imply moral excellence or beneficial quality

Virtues - II
Approach to Normative Ethics

- Practiced at all times
  - *habitual excellence and character*
  - must be continuously practiced in order for any person to maintain oneself in virtue
- Virtues are habits. Once acquired, they become characteristic of a person

Value

- The relative worth placed on some virtuous behavior.
- What has value to one person may not have value to another.
- Value is a standard of conduct.
- Values are used for judging the goodness or badness of some action.
- Values are standards by which we measure goodness in our lives.

Values

- *Intrinsic Value*
  - something that has value in & of itself

- *Instrumental Value*
  - something that helps to give value to something else
    - money is valuable for what it can buy

Notes

Virtues & Values - I

- Commitment
- Conscientiousness
- Cooperativeness
- Courage
- Discernment
- Fairness

Virtues & Values - II

- Faith
- Fidelity
- Freedom
- Generosity
- Happiness
- Honesty/Trustworthiness/Truth-Telling

Virtues & Values - III

- Hopefulness
- Humility
- Integrity
- Kindness
- Prudence
- Respect
- Self-respect

Values May Change

If one's basic needs for food, water, clothing & housing have not been met, one's values may change in such a way that a friendship, for example, might be sacrificed if one's basic needs can be better met as a result of the sacrifice.

Values Can Change

- People make value judgments & choices among alternatives.
- Values one so dearly proclaims may change as needs change.
- Motivating power of a person's actions are a necessity of survival.
- Values give purpose to each life. They make up one's moral character.

Differing Values

If mom's estate is being squandered at the end of life – a family member financially well-off may want to hold on to mom despite the financial drain on her estate. Another family member financially struggling to survive may more readily see the futility of expensive medical care & find it easier to let go.

Notes

Situational Ethics - I

- Situational ethics refers to a particular view of ethics, in which absolute standards are considered less important than the requirements of a particular situation.
- The importance of a particular value may vary as one's situation changes.

Situational Ethics - II

- Moral values & moral character can be compromised when faced with difficult choices.
- Good people behave differently in different situations.
- Good people sometimes do bad things
- One's moral character can sometimes change as circumstances change
  – thus the term *situational ethics*.

Sustaining Life: Situational Ethics

A decision not to use extraordinary means to sustain life of an unknown 84 year old "may" result in a different decision if the 84 year old is one's mother.

Ethical Decision-Making

Ethical decision-making is the process of deciding, what the right thing to do is in the event of a moral dilemma.

Case: High in the Andes - I

Those who survived the plane crash high in the Andes Mountains were faced with some difficult survival decisions. Their need to survive illustrates to what lengths one may go in certain situations in order to survive (see text page 28).

High in the Andes - II

- How might you change as circumstances change?
- Describe how your consultative advice might change based on the patient's needs, beliefs, & family influences.

Notes

A Case of Paternalism

The family physician does not fully inform Mr. Smith as to the seriousness of his illness and how the consequences of the various alternative treatments might affect his life style.

Discuss the ethical & legal issues.

Ethical & Legal Issues

- Ethical issues
  - Autonomy
  - Paternalism

- Legal issues
  - Informed consent
    - Refer to Chapter 12

Practical Suggestions

- Be a good listener
  - Listen with the intent to learn not to find fault or argue.
  - Listen to contribute & resolve ethical dilemmas.
- Believe in good values
- Become virtuous
  - by practicing good values until they become habits.

Notes

Chapter 2
Contemporary Ethical Dilemmas

Learning Objectives

- Improve understanding of common ethical dilemmas in health care settings
  - Abortion
  - HIV/AIDS
  - Artificial Insemination
  - Organ Donations
  - Research – Experimentation – Clinical Trials
  - Sterilization
  - Wrongful – Birth, Life, & Conception

ABORTION
Ethical & Legal Issues

- Rights of the Woman
  - Autonomy
- Rights of the Fetus
- Rights of the Spouse
- Rights of the State
  - protecting life

Pro-choice v Pro-life

- Whose decision is it?
  - Mother
  - Spouse
  - State
- When does life begin?
- Moral & religious aspects?
- Constitutional aspects?

Abortion

U.S. Supreme Court Decisions

1973 - *Roe v. Wade*

- Woman's right to privacy.
- Recognition of state protecting the unborn.
  - <u>First Trimester</u>: abortion decision between woman & physician.
  - <u>Second Trimester</u>: state may reasonably regulate abortion procedure.
  - <u>Third Trimester</u>: state may prohibit all abortions except those deemed necessary to protect maternal life or health.

1973 - *Doe v. Bolton*

- Struck down the following procedural requirements imposed by state statutes:
  - residency
  - performance of abortion in hospital accredited by Joint Commission
  - approval by committee of medical staff
  - consultations

1976 - *Danforth v. Planned Parenthood*

- Unconstitutional to require "all" women under 18 to obtain parental consent.

1977 - *Maher v. Roe*

- States may refuse to spend public funds to provide non-therapeutic abortions.

Notes

1979 - *Colautti v. Franklin*

- States may seek to protect a fetus which a physician has determined could survive outside the womb.

1979 - *Bellotti v. Baird-Parental Consent*

- Statute requiring parental consent for woman under 18 unconstitutional.

1980 - *Harris v. McRae*

- Upheld Hyde Amendment restricting use of federal funds for Medicaid abortions.

1981 - *H. L. v. Matheson*

- Utah statute upheld: requiring a physician to notify parents or guardian of a minor on whom an abortion is to be performed.
- State may not constitutionally legislate blanket un-reviewable power of parents to veto daughter's right to abortion.

1983 - *City of Akron v. Akron Center for Reproductive Health*

- States cannot mandate:
  - abortions for women more than 3 months pregnant must be performed in a hospital.
  - that only physicians competent to provide information & counselling.
  - regulations to influence woman's informed choice between abortion & childbirth.

1989 - *Webster v. Reproductive Health Services*

- Missouri statute upheld:
  - public employees & public facilities may not be used in performing or assisting in abortions unnecessary to save mother's life.
  - physicians should conduct viability tests before performing an abortion.

Notes

1991 - *Rust v. Sullivan*

- Federal regulations prohibiting abortion counseling by family planning clinics that receive funds under Title X do not violate constitutional rights of pregnant women.

1992 - *Planned Parenthood v. Casey*

- Supreme Court reaffirmed:
  - constitutional right of women to have abortion before viability of fetus.
  - state's power to restrict abortions after fetal viability, provided law contains exceptions for pregnancies that endanger woman's health.
  - state's interests from outset of pregnancy in protecting health of woman & life of fetus.

Casey, Cont.

- Court will evaluate permissibility of state abortion rules based on whether they unduly burden woman's ability to obtain an abortion.
  - A rule is undue burden if its purpose or effect is to place substantial obstacle in the path of woman seeking abortion before the fetus attains viability.
  - Undue burden to require notification of the husband of the woman's decision to abort the fetus.

Casey, Cont.

- Supreme Court ruled not an undue burden:
- to inform woman of nature of abortion procedure & risks.
- to offer information on fetus & alternatives to abortion.
- for woman to give informed consent prior to abortion procedure.

Casey, Cont.

- to require parental consent for minor seeking abortion.
  - must provide for judicial bypass option if minor does not wish or cannot obtain parental consent
- require 24-hour waiting period prior to abortion.

1998 - *Women's Medical Professional Corp. v. Voinovich*

- Supreme Court denied *certiorari* for first partial-birth case to reach federal appellate courts.
- 6th Circuit Court of Appeals held statute banning any use of D&X ("Dilation and Extraction") procedure unconstitutionally vague.

2000 - *Stenberg v. Carhart*

- Supreme Court struck down Nebraska ban on "partial birth abortion."

2003 - Partial Birth Abortion Ban Made Law

- President Bush signed 1st federal restrictions banning late term partial birth abortions.
- Both houses of Congress passed ban.
- Ban permits no exceptions when woman's health at risk or fetus has life threatening disabilities.

2006 – Supreme Court Hears Abortion Arguments

U.S. Supreme Court Justices heard oral arguments on November 8 in what may be two of the most significant abortion rights cases in decades. The dispute involves Congress's ban on partial birth abortion.

Morality of Abortion

- Not a legal or constitutional issue
- Matter of
  - philosophy
  - ethics
  - theology

Morality of Abortion, Con't

- Reasonable people can, & do, adhere to vastly divergent convictions & principles
- Obligation to define liberty of all, not to mandate a particular moral code

AIDS

- Deadliest epidemic in human history.
- 1st case appeared in literature in 1981.
- more than 21 million people have died from AIDS.
- AIDS caused by Human Immunodeficiency Virus (HIV).
- Highly contagious blood-borne virus.
- Destroys body's capacity to ward off bacteria.

Confidentiality
Disclosure of Physician's IV Status

The physician cut his hand with a scalpel while he was assisting another physician. Because of the uncertainty that blood had been transferred from Doe's hand wound to the patient through an open surgical incision, he agreed to have a blood test for HIV. His blood tested positive for HIV and he withdrew himself from participation in further surgical procedures.

Discuss the ethical & legal issues.

Confidentiality- Ethical Issues

- Physician's right to privacy v. patients right to know
- Utilitarianism
- advocates the greatest good for the greatest number
- Conscientiousness
  - a person who has moral integrity & a strict regard for doing the right thing

Confidentiality – Legal Decision

Failure to notify the patients at risk could result in the spread of the HIV virus to other non-infected individuals through sexual contact and through exposure to other body fluids. Doe's name was not revealed to the patients, only the fact that a resident physician who participated in their care had tested HIV-positive. "No principle is more deeply embedded in the law than that expressed in the maxim *Salus populi suprema lex,* . . . (the welfare of the people is the supreme law).

Artificial Insemination

- Injection of seminal fluid into a woman to induce pregnancy
- Homologous artificial insemination
  - semen of spouse used to impregnate
- Heterologous artificial insemination
  - semen from donor other than husband

Organ Donations

- Federal regulations require hospitals implement
  - protocols regarding an organization's organ procurement responsibilities
  - specific notification duties
  - requirements informing families of potential donors
  - sensitivity in dealing with families
  - educating hospital staff on organ donation
  - facilitate timely donation & transplantation

Human Research

- Ethical principles
  - Respect for person
  - Beneficence
    - Hippocratic Oath – physicians to benefit patients
  - Justice
  - Personal autonomy
  - Self-determination

Justice

- Each person to be treated equally.
- Each person to treated
  - according to need?
  - according to value to society (societal contribution)?
  - according to merit?

Nuremberg Code & Declaration of Helsinki

- International code of ethics
  - governs human research
- Result of Nazi medical atrocities
- Requires human subjects be fully informed

Federal Regulations Control Experiments Involving

- Drugs
- Medical devices
- Medical procedures

Conducting Clinical Trials

- Organization must provide for:
  - education in ethical decision-making
  - nurse participation in ethical decision-making
  - on-going monitoring of approved protocols

Institutional Review Board

- Federal regulations require hospital-based Institutional Review Board (IRB)
- IRB Functions
  - review proposed research studies
  - approve protocols for research
  - conduct research oversight

Informed Consent

- Organizations must disclose
  - risks, benefits & treatment alternatives
- Determine competency of patient consent
- Obtain written consent from patient
- Disclose treatment costs
- Educate Staff
  - potential side effects of treatments
  - implementation of protocols
  - monitoring of protocols

Sterilization

- Elective Sterilization
  - Voluntary sterilization
- Therapeutic Sterilization
  - Performed to preserve life or health
- Eugenic Sterilization
  - Involuntary sterilization - described in statutes
    - mentally deficient
    - feeble-minded

Wrongful Birth

- A claim that but for a breach of duty by the defendant(s) (e.g., improper sterilization), child would not have been born.

Wrongful Life

- A claim brought by parent(s) or child who claims to have suffered harm as a result being born.

Wrongful Conception

- A claim by parents of unexpected child based on allegation that conception resulted from a
  - negligent sterilization procedures
  - defective contraceptive device

Chapter 3: Health Care Ethics Committee

Notes

Chapter 3
Health Care Ethics Committee

Learning Objectives

- Understand structure, development & goals of ethics committees.
- Describe functions of ethics committees.
- Describe expanding role of ethics committees.
- Understand concept of reasoning & decision making.

Committee Composition

- ethicists
- educators
- caregivers
- legal advisors
- political leaders
- religious leaders
- corporate leaders

Goals of Ethics Committee

- Policy & Procedure Development
- Consultation & Conflict Resolution
- Education
- Promote Patient Rights

Policy & Procedure Development - I

- Determine the goals & responsibilities of the ethics committee
  - which types of cases will be addressed
- Determine consultation process
  - How to access consultation services
- Develop consultation guidelines

Policy & Procedure Development - II

- Education
  - recognize time commitment
  - include training in philosophy, religion, medicine, & law
  - include formal training & experience in clinical ethics
  - develop & distribute appropriate materials for committee members, caregivers, patients & family

Policy & Procedure Development - III

- Committee function
  - forum for discussion
- Recommendations should be advisory, not mandatory
  - recognize the potential for harm as well as benefit

Consultation & Conflict Resolution

- Resource for patients, family, & staff in resolving ethical dilemmas.
- Provide guidance, not decisions.
- Strive to achieve consensus when addressing care dilemmas.

Education

- Ethics committee members
- Community
- Patients & family
- Staff
  - ambulatory care facilities
  - home health agencies
  - long term care facilities
  - physician office practices

Notes

Notes

Promote Patient Rights

- Right to self-determination (autonomy)
  - accept or reject care & treatment
- Right to ethics committee consultation

Conducting a Consultation

- identify the dilemma
- identify relevant facts
- identify stakeholders
- identify moral issues
- identify legal issues
- conduct consultation

Expanding Role of Ethics Committees
Internal Ethical Issues

- Dilemma of blind drug trials
  - Who gets the placebo?
- Informed consent
  - Have patients been adequately informed of proposed treatment plan?
- Privacy & Confidentiality
  - What medical information should be shared with the patient's family & other caregivers?

Expanding Role of Ethics Committees, External Ethical Issues

- Malpractice insurance rates
  - its economic strain & drain on limited resources
- Reimbursement issues
  - uninsured
  - managed care
  - denial of care

Convening the Ethics Committee Rules to Follow

- Serve as a *resource* when there are no clear choices.
- Be *sensitive* to patient & family values.
- *Search* for the best path to conflict resolution.
- *Assist* family in reaching for consensus.
- *Educate & guide* the process without personal biases.

Facing Ethical Dilemmas Guidelines

- Seek to diagnose before you prescribe.
- *Not sure what to do* – discuss your dilemma with other committee members.
- Do not impose your beliefs on others.
- Help guide others to make choices.
- Ask the patient how you might help.

Notes

Notes

Reasoning

- Reason involves
  - capacity for logical inference
  - conduct inquiry, evaluate, criticize, deliberate, & solve problems
  - reach an understanding of self & others

Forms of Reasoning

- *Partial reasoning*
  - bias for or against a person
  - based on one's relationship with that person

- *Circular Reasoning*
  - When a person sees no need for deliberation
    - "I have already made up my mind – don't confuse me with the facts."

Decision-Making Process

- Process of deciding
  - what is the right thing to do
- Dilemmas occur when there are alternative choices
- Variety of value beliefs
  - patients
  - family members
  - caregivers

Decision-Making Process

- Limited resources affect decisions
  - Reaching agreement may mean
    - sacrificing one's personal values
- Consensus building occurs when people reason together

Text Case: Patient Refuses Blood

- Should the physician refuse to treat this patient? Explain your answer.
- Should the family have a right to override the patient's decision to refuse blood? Explain your answer.

Text Case: A Son's Guilt—A Father's Wishes

- Discuss the ethical dilemmas in this case.
- Discuss the issues and the role of the ethics committee in this case.

Notes

Chapter 4: End of Life Dilemmas

Notes

Chapter 4
End of Life Dilemmas

When we finally know we are dying,
And all other sentient beings are dying with us,
We start to have a burning,
almost heartbreaking sense
of the fragility and preciousness of each moment
and each being,
and from this can grow
a deep, clear, limitless compassion for all beings.

Sogyal Rinpoche

Learning Objectives

• Understand & describe "end of life" dilemmas.

• Present overview of one's right to self-determination.

Notes

- Understand & describe
  - Euthanasia
  - Physician Assisted Suicide
  - Oregon's Death with Dignity Act
  - Patient Self-Determination Act of 1990
  - Advance Directives
  - Appointed Decision-Makers
  - Futility of Treatment
  - Withdrawal of Treatment

Introduction

- Dreams of immortality
- Race to prevent & cure illness
- Advances in medicine prolongs life
- Process of dying prolonged
- Artificial body organs
- Exotic machines
- Medications

Self-Determination - Significant Events

- **1976**   NJ Supreme Ct. permission to remove Quinlan from a ventilator.

- **1980**   Hemlock Society is formed to advocate for physician-assisted dying.

- **1983**   California: first durable power of attorney legislation.

Significant Events

- **1990** Cruzan could have feeding tube removed
  - Dr. Kevorkian's suicide machine
  - Congress passed the Patient Self-Determination Act

- **1994** Oregon vote legalized physician-assisted suicide

Significant Events

- **1996** Constitutional right under 14th Amendment for terminally ill person to receive help from a physician in dying

- **1997** Physician assisted suicide, legal medical option for terminally ill in Oregon
  - Kevorkian charged with murder in Michigan

Significant Events

- **1998** Oregon voters reaffirm support for Death with Dignity Act
  - Michigan voters defeat ballot measure legalizing physician suicide
- **1999** Kevorkian convicted of 2nd degree murder
- **2001** District Court Judge upholds Oregon "Death with Dignity Act"

Notes

Notes

Euthanasia

- Greek: *euthanatos*, euthanasia, meaning "good death" or "easy death"
- Euthanasia: "the mercy killing of the hopelessly ill, injured or incapacitated."

Active or Passive Euthanasia

- *Active euthanasia*: intentional commission of an act, which results in death.
  - *administration of a lethal dose of medication*
- *Passive euthanasia*: when life-saving treatment (e.g.respirator) is
  - *withdrawn*
  - *withheld*

Voluntary or Involuntary Euthanasia

- *Voluntary*: suffering person makes decision to die.

- *Involuntary*: person other than the incurable makes decision to terminate life.

Value Questions Face Courts
Involuntary Euthanasia

- Who should decide to withhold or withdraw treatment?
- On what factors should a decision be based?
- Are there viable standards to guide courts?
- Should criminal sanctions be imposed on a person assisting in ending life?
- When does death occur?

Constitutional Considerations
Autonomy

- *Schloendorff v. Society of New York Hospital*
  - Every human being of adult years has a right to determine what shall be done with his own body & the surgeon who performs an operation without his patient's consent commits an assault for which he is liable for damages.

In re Storar

Every human being of adult years & sound mind has the right to determine what shall be done with his or her own body.

In re Quinlan

- Constitutional right to privacy protects patient's right to self-determination.

- A state's interest does not justify interference with one's right to refuse treatment.

Superintendent of Belchertown State School v. Saikewicz

- Saikewicz allowed to refuse treatment.
- Questions of life & death with regard to an incompetent should be the responsibility of the courts.
- Court took a "dim view of any attempt to shift ultimate decision-making responsibility away from duly established courts of proper jurisdiction to any committee, panel, or group, ad hoc or permanent."

In re Dinnerstein

- "No code" orders are valid to prevent the use of artificial resuscitative measures on incompetent terminally ill patients.

In re Spring

- Patient's mental impairment & his or her medical prognosis with or without treatment must be considered prior to seeking judicial approval to withdraw or withhold treatment from an incompetent patient.

Court involvement when:

- Family members disagree as to incompetent's wishes.
- Physicians disagree on the prognosis.
- A patient's wishes are unknown because he or she always has been incompetent.
- Evidence exists of wrongful motives or malpractice.

Defining Death

- Irreversible cessation of brain function constitutes death.
- American Medical Association in 1974 accepted that death occurs when there is "irreversible cessation of all brain functions including the brain stem."

Notes

Prolongation of Life

- Evidence: patient's intention to reject prolongation of life by artificial means:
  - persistence of statements regarding an individual's beliefs.
  - desirability of the commitment to those beliefs
  - seriousness with which such statements were made.
  - inferences that may be drawn from surrounding circumstances.

Legislative Response

- After Cruzan decision, states began to draft new legislation in the areas of living wills, durable powers of attorney, health care proxies, & surrogate decision making.

- Chief Justice Dore, Washington Supr. Ct.,
  - response to right-to-die issues can be better addressed by legislature

Physician Assisted Suicide

U.S. Supreme Court rejected Kevorkian's argument that assisted suicide is a constitutional right.

Physician Assisted Suicide, cont.

- U.S. Supreme Court, in two unanimous & separate decisions, ruled:

  - Washington & New York laws prohibiting assisted suicide are constitutional.

  - States can allow doctors to assist in suicide of their terminally ill patients.

Criminalizing Assisted Suicide

- Supreme Court in *Quill v. Vacco*, determined New York had valid reasons for distinguishing between refusing treatment & assisting suicide:
  - prohibiting intentional killing & preserving life.
  - preventing suicide.
  - maintaining physician's role as patient's healer; & protecting vulnerable people from indifference, prejudice, & psychological & financial pressure to end their lives.

Washington v. Glucksberg

- Court held assisted suicide not a liberty protected by Constitution's due process clause.

- Majority of states ban assisted suicide.

Notes

Assisted Suicide
Profound Questions

- medicine
- medical ethics
- theology
- sociology
- far-reaching public policy issues

Oregon's Death with Dignity Act

- Allows terminally ill Oregon residents to obtain lethal dose of medication from his or her physician.
- Legalizes physician-assisted suicide.
- Prohibits physician or other person from directly administering medication to end another's life.

Patient Self-Determination Act of 1990

- Patients have right to formulate advance directives.

- Health care providers receiving federal funds under Medicare need to comply with regulations.

Living Will

An instrument or legal document that describes treatments an individual wishes or does not wish to receive should he or she become incapacitated & unable to communicate treatment decisions.

Durable Power of Attorney

A legal device that permits one individual known as "principal" to give to another person "attorney-in-fact" authority to act on his or her behalf. Attorney-in-fact is authorized to handle banking & real estate affairs, incur expenses, pay bills . . . .

Durable Power of Attorney for Health Care

An agent makes health & personal care decisions for the patient in the event the patient becomes unable to make his or her own decisions.

Notes

Appointed Decision-Makers

- _Guardianship_: legal mechanism by which court declares a person incompetent & appoints a guardian.
- _Health Care Proxy_: a document that allows a person to appoint a health care agent to make treatment decisions in event he or she becomes incompetent & is unable to make decisions for him- or herself.
- _Surrogate Decision-Maker_: Agent who acts on behalf of a patient who lacks capacity to participate in a decision.

Futility of Treatment

Physician recognizes that effect of treatment will be of no benefit to the patient.

Withdrawal of Treatment –When

- the patient is in a terminal condition.
- reasonable expectation of imminent death.
- patient is in a non-cognitive state with no reasonable possibility of regaining cognitive function.
- restoration of cardiac function will last but for a brief period.

Removal of Life-Support Equipment

May be a duty to provide life-sustaining equipment in immediate aftermath of cardiopulmonary arrest, however, there is no duty to continue its use once it becomes futile.

Withdrawal of Feeding Tube – I
Terry Schiavo

Twenty-seven year old Terry Schiavo suffered a cardiac arrest in February of 1990. She never regained consciousness. Since 1990, she lived in nursing homes and was fed & hydrated by tubes. In May of 1998, Michael, Terry's husband, petitioned the court for guardianship to authorize termination of life-prolonging procedures. The Schindlers, Terry's parents, opposed the petition.

Schiavo II

- Michael contended his wife never wanted to be kept alive artificially.
- Terry's parents told justices that their son-in-law is trying to rush her death so he can inherit her estate & be free to marry another woman.

Notes

_____
_____
_____
_____
_____
_____
_____
_____
_____
_____
_____
_____
_____
_____
_____
_____
_____
_____
_____
_____
_____
_____
_____
_____
_____
_____
_____
_____
_____
_____
_____
_____

Schiavo – III

A guardianship court issued a written order authorizing discontinuance of artificial life support. The trial court found by convincing evidence that Terry was in a persistent vegetative state & that she would elect to cease life-prolonging procedures if she were competent to do so. This order was affirmed on appeal.

Schiavo – IV

On October 21, 2003, the Florida Legislature enacted chapter 2003-418, which the Governor signed into law, & issued executive order No. 03-201 to stay the continued withholding of nutrition & hydration. The nutrition & hydration tube was reinserted pursuant to the Governor's executive order.

Schiavo – V
Florida Law Chapter 2003-418

Section 1. (1) The Governor shall have the authority to issue a one-time stay to prevent the withholding of nutrition . . . :

   (a) That patient has no written advance directive;

   (b) The court has found that patient to be in a persistent vegetative state;

   (c) That patient has had nutrition and hydration withheld; &

   (d) A member of . . . family has challenged the withholding of nutrition . . . .

Schiavo – VI

The circuit court entered a judgment on May 6, 2004, in favor of Michael. The circuit court found that chapter 2003-418 was unconstitutional because it allowed the Governor to encroach upon judicial power & to retroactively abolish Terry's vested right to privacy.

Schiavo – VII

This case is not about the aspirations loving parents have for their children. It is about Terry's right to make her own decision. It is unfortunate that when families cannot agree, the best forum for a personal decision is a public courtroom & the decision-maker is a judge; the law, however, provides no better solution to protect the interests of promoting the value of life.

Schiavo – VIII

The court stated we are a nation of laws & we must govern our decisions by the rule of law & not by our emotions. Our hearts comprehend the grief so fully demonstrated by Terry's family members. But our hearts are not the law. What is in the Constitution always must prevail over emotion. Our oaths as judges require that this principle is our polestar, and it alone.

Notes

Notes

Schiavo – IX
Separation of Powers

If the Legislature with the assent of the Governor can do what was attempted here, the judicial branch would be subordinated to the final directive of the other branches. Also subordinated would be the rights of individuals, including the well established privacy right to self determination. No court judgment could ever be considered truly final and no constitutional right truly secure, because the precedent of this case would hold to the contrary. Vested rights could be stripped away based on popular clamor.
Bush v. Schiavo, No. SC04-925 (Fla.App. 2004).

Schiavo – X

The U.S. Supreme Court, on January 24, 2005, refused to reinstate the Florida law passed to keep Terry connected to a feeding tube, clearing the way for it to be removed.

Discuss the ethical & legal issues.

Schiavo – XI

• Ethical Issues
  – Autonomy

• Legal Issues
  – Guardianship
  – Right to Self-Determination
    • See Chapter 7

Patient's Wishes - I

A sister was not entitled to an order enjoining her brother & sister from implementing their mother's "living will" in which their mother, Mrs. D, directed the withdrawal of life-sustaining medical procedures in the event she should have a terminal & irreversible condition. Mrs. D specifically prohibited her daughters from making decisions about life-sustaining procedures.

Patient's Wishes - II

Mrs. D did not want her life to be artificially prolonged. If at any time she should be diagnosed as having an incurable disease or illness in the absence of her ability to give directions regarding the use of life-sustaining procedures, it was her intention that her declaration be honored by her family & physician/s as the final expression of her legal right to refuse medical or surgical treatment.

Discuss the ethical & legal issues.

Patient's Wishes - III

- Ethical Issues
  - Autonomy
- Legal Issues
  - Case: *Pettis v. Smith*, 880 So.2d 145 (La. App. 2004)
  - Patient Self-Determination Act
    - Refer to Chapter 7

Notes

Notes

Do Not Resuscitate Orders

- Orders given by a physician, indicating that in the event of a cardiac or respiratory arrest, "no" resuscitative measures should be used.

- Given when quality of life has been so diminished that "heroic" rescue methods are no longer in patient's best interests.

Spousal Rights in Decision-Making

- Discuss the four-part test for determining the patient's ability to make a decision.
- Do you agree with the court's decision?
- Should the concern of the mother & sister have carried more weight in removing custody from Mrs. Martin?

Men Don't Cry

- Remembering Annie in the summary case in Chapter 1, do you think Mark is capable of making end of life decisions for Sunshine? Explain your answer.

- Should Sunshine appoint Mark as her health care surrogate decision maker? Explain your answer.

Notes

```
_____
_____
_____
_____
_____
_____
_____
_____
_____
_____
_____
_____
_____
_____
_____
_____
_____
_____
_____
_____
_____
_____
_____
_____
_____
_____
_____
_____
_____
_____
_____
_____
_____
_____
_____
_____
_____
_____
_____
_____
_____
_____
```

Chapter 5
Development of Law

Learning Objectives

- Understand development of law
- Describe the legal system
- Describe sources of law
- Describe 3 branches of government
- Understand, *separation of powers*

Development of Law

- Tradition
- Culture
- Customs
- Beliefs

Notes

_____

_____

_____

_____

_____

_____

_____

_____

_____

_____

_____

_____

_____

_____

_____

_____

_____

_____

_____

_____

_____

_____

_____

_____

_____

_____

_____

_____

_____

_____

_____

_____

_____

_____

_____

_____

Why Laws Change

- Political Climate
- Social Change
- Religious Beliefs
- Values Change

Laws

General rules of conduct enforced by government.

Categories of Law

- *Public law*
  - relationships between individuals & government

- *Private law*
  - relationships between individuals

Sources of Law

- Common Law

- Statutory Law

- Administrative Law

Common Law

- Derived from Judicial Decisions

  - Origins - English common law
  - Responds to issues beyond written law

- Common often differs State to State

Common Law, cont.

- Common-law principles prevail
  - unless a statute governs

- Judicial decision in one state does not set precedent for another

Notes

Statutory Law

- Written law - emanates from legislative bodies
- Courts often interpret how various statutes apply to each set of facts
- *U.S. Constitution* highest in hierarchy of enacted law

Statutory Law, *cont.*
Bill of Rights

- Amendments to the U.S. constitution were added to protect rights of citizens.
  - Right to privacy
  - Equal protection
  - Freedom of speech
  - Freedom of religion

Administrative Law

- Public law is issued by admininistrative agencies to direct enacted laws
- *Administrative Procedures Act*
  - procedures under which federal agencies operate
- Rules & Regulations administered within intent of law
- Regulations subject to judicial review

Government Organization
Legislative Branch

- enacts laws
- amend or repeal existing legislation
- create new legislation

Government Organization
Judicial Branch

- Resolves legal disputes
- Supreme Court
  - nation's highest court
  - 8 associate justices & 1 chief justice

Government Organization
Executive Branch

- Administers & enforce the law
- Executive Power vested in the President
- Cabinet advises the President

Notes

Notes

Separation of Powers

- System of checks & balances
- No one branch of government dominant over other two

Federal Department

- Department of Health & Human Services

    - cabinet-level department
    - responsible for carrying out national health & human services policy
    - main source of regulations affecting the health care industry

Notes

Chapter 6
Introduction to Law

1

Tort Law
A Definition

A wrong, other than a breach of contract, committed against a person or property for which a court provides a remedy, generally in the form of monetary damages.

Objectives of Tort Law

- Preservation of peace between individuals.
- Fault-finding for wrongdoing.
- Acts as a deterrence to wrongful acts.
- Indemnify injured person(s).

Negligence

Commission or omission of an act that a reasonably prudent person would or would not do under given circumstances.

Commission of an Act

- Administering the wrong drug
- Administering the wrong drug dosage
- Mislabeling a drug
- Performing wrong-sided surgery

Omission of an Act

- Failure to administer medications
- Failure to follow up on critical lab tests
- Failure to obtain consent
- Failure to monitor a patient

Malpractice

- Negligence of a professional person
  - Surgeon who conducts surgery on the wrong body part.
  - Nurse who administers wrong medication injuring patient.
  - Pharmacist who mislabels a medication & the patient is harmed.

Criminal Negligence

- Reckless disregard for the safety of another.
- Willful indifference to injury that could follow an act.

Forms of Negligence

- Malfeasance

- Misfeasance

- Nonfeasance

Notes

Notes

Malfeasance

- Execution of an unlawful or improper act

  - performing a partial birth abortion when prohibited by law.
  - Performing a procedure without having the appropriate credentials.

Misfeasance

- Improper performance of an act

  - Wrong-sided surgery
  - leaving an instrument in the patient's body

Nonfeasance

- Failure to act when there is a duty to act
  - failure to prescribe antibiotics when indicated.
  - failure to respond to emergency call.

Elements of Negligence

- Duty to Care
- Breach of Duty
- Injury/Actual Damages
- Proximate Cause/Causation
  - Foreseeability

I. Duty to Care

Legal obligation of care imposed on one to safeguard rights of others

Standard of Care

- Actual performance of an individual in a given situation will be measured against what a reasonably prudent person would or would not have done.
- Conduct expected in a given situation.
- Care provided in acceptable manner.
- Care a "reasonably prudent person" would provide acting under the same or similar circumstances.

Reasonably Prudent Person

Concept that describes nonexistent, hypothetical person who is put forward as community ideal of what would be considered reasonable behavior.

Ethicists & Standard of Care

Physician expert was allowed to base an opinion on breach of standard of care upon violation of ethical standard established by the American Medical Association.

Neade v. Portes, 710 N.E.2d 418 (Ill. App. Ct. 1999)

Duty to Hire Competent Employees

A nurse was hired sight unseen over telephone an applicant who falsely stated in his application that he was a licensed LPN.

In reality, he was not an LPN & he had committed 56 criminal offenses of theft & assaulted a resident. Your verdict?

Judgment for the Plaintiff

Nursing center failed in its "duty to care" by not validating the nurse's license.

Duty to Provide Timely Care

Wrongful death of 19-year-old. Action was brought against the hospital; the emergency department physician, Dr. Gerdes; and the thoracic surgeon on call, Dr. McCool.

Hastings v. Baton Rouge Hospital

II. Breach of Duty

- Must be a deviation from recognized standard of care.
- Must be failure to adhere to an obligation.

Notes

Notes

Breach Of Duty
Hastings v. Baton Rouge Hospital

- Breach of duty occurred when the physician failed to respond to his/her on-call duties.

III. Injury

- Actual damages must be established.
- Without injury damages cannot be awarded.

Injury in *Hastings Case*

- In *Hastings*, the patient's death was a direct result of the physician's breach of duty.

IV. Causation

Must be a reasonable, close, and causal connection between the defendant's negligent conduct and the resulting damages suffered.

Causation
In *Hastings*

In the ordinary course of events, a person does not bleed to death in a hospital emergency department over a two-hour period without some surgical intervention.

Foreseeability

Reasonable anticipation that harm or injury is likely to result from an act or an omission to act.

Notes

_____

_____

_____

_____

_____

_____

_____

_____

_____

_____

_____

_____

_____

_____

_____

_____

_____

_____

_____

_____

_____

_____

_____

_____

_____

_____

_____

_____

_____

_____

_____

_____

_____

_____

_____

_____

_____

_____

_____

_____

_____

_____

Foreseeability
In *Hastings*

It was highly probable that the patient would die if the bleeding was not stopped. "The broad test of negligence is what a reasonably prudent person would foresee & would do in the light of this foresight under the circumstances."

Test for Foreseeability

The test for foreseeability is whether a person of ordinary prudence and intelligence should have anticipated danger to others caused by his or her negligent act.

Comedy of Errors
Niles v. City of San Rafael.

Expert testimony by two neurosurgeons during the trial indicated that the patient's chances of recovery would have been very good if Niles had been admitted promptly. This testimony placed the proximate cause of the injury with the hospital.

Ethical Lesson in Niles

If the "ethical theories, principles and values" discussed in Chapter 1 had been adopted, in place, understood, and practiced, Kelly Niles would be leading a normal life today.

Intentional Torts

- Assault and Battery
- False Imprisonment
- Defamation of Character
- Invasion of Privacy
- Infliction of Mental Distress

Assault and Battery

- *Assault* – deliberate threat, coupled with apparent ability to do physical harm to another. Actual contact not necessary.

- *Battery* – intentional touching of another's person in socially impermissible manner without person's consent.

Notes

Notes

_____

Assault

1. Person attempting to touch another unlawfully must possess apparent present ability to commit battery.

2. Person threatened must be aware of or have actual knowledge of an immediate threat of a battery and must fear it.

False Imprisonment

Unlawful restraint of individual's personal liberty or unlawful restraining or confining an individual.

Invasion of Privacy

- Right to
  - be left alone
  - be free from unwarranted publicity
  - be free from exposure to public view
  - be free from unwarranted intrusions into a one's personal affairs
  - personal privacy
  - have records/kept confidential

Infliction of Mental Distress

Conduct that is so outrageous that it goes beyond bounds tolerated by decent society.

Criminal Law

- *Crime* - any social harm defined and made punishable by law
- *Purpose of criminal law*
  - maintain public order and safety.
  - protect the individual.
  - use punishment as a deterrent to crime.
  - rehabilitate the criminal for return to society.

Classification of Crimes

- *Misdemeanor* - an offense punishable by less than one year in jail and/or a fine (e.g., petty larceny).

- *Felony* - is a much more serious crime (e.g., rape, murder) and is generally punishable by imprisonment in a state or federal penitentiary for more than one year.

Notes

Billing Scam

A pharmacist dispensed the generic equivalent of a drug & billed for the higher cost brand name.

Discuss the ethical & legal issues.

40

Ethical & Legal Issues

- Ethical Issues
  - Truth telling
    - Refer to Chapter 1
  - Professional codes of ethics
    - Refer to Chapter 9
- Legal Issues
  - Fraud

41

Self-Referrals

Dr. L ordered unnecessary highly expensive esoteric lab tests for his patients. Dr. L referred his patients to a private lab, in which he had 30% ownership.

Discuss the ethical & legal issues.

42

Ethical & Legal Issues

- Ethical Issues
  - Truthfulness
    - Refer to Chapter 1
  - Professional codes of ethics
    - Refer to Chapter 9
- Legal Issues
  - Fraud

43

4 Paralyzed - Botox Scam

A toxin manufacturer has been implicated in a Botox scam that apparently left four people in South Florida paralyzed after being injected with a substance they mistakenly thought was the anti-wrinkle drug. The lab expressed its deep concern that its research chemical was illegally injected in humans.

Discuss the ethical & legal issues.

44

Ethical & Legal Issues

- Ethical Issues
  - *Nonmaleficence* - ethical principle requiring caregivers to avoid causing patients harm.
  - Truthfulness
    - Refer to Chapter 1
- Legal Issues
  - Criminal Issues
    - Fraud
    - Criminal Negligence

45

Notes

Contracts

Contract - a special kind of agreement, either written or oral, that involves legally binding obligations between two or more parties

Elements of a Contract

1. Offer/Communication
2. Consideration
3. Acceptance

Kinds of Contracts

- Employment Contracts
- Exclusive Contracts
- Commercial Ethics and Non Competition Agreements

Trial Procedures - I

- Pleadings
- Discovery of Evidence
- Preparation of Witnesses
- The Court
- The Jury

Trial Procedures - II

- Subpoenas
- Opening Statements
- Burden of Proof
- Evidence
- Defense Against Recovery

Trial Procedures - III

- Closing Statements
- Judge's Charge to the Jury
- Jury Deliberation
- Damages
- Appeals

Notes

Notes

_____
_____
_____
_____
_____
_____
_____
_____
_____
_____
_____
_____
_____
_____
_____
_____
_____
_____
_____
_____
_____
_____
_____
_____
_____
_____
_____
_____
_____
_____
_____
_____

Pleadings

- Summons and Complaint
- Answer
- Bill of Particulars

Discovery of Evidence

- Process of investigating the facts of a case before trial.

Objectives of Discovery

- Obtain evidence that might not be obtainable at time of trial.
- Isolate & narrow issues for trial.
- Gather knowledge of existence of additional evidence that may be admissible at trial.
- Obtain leads to enable discovering party to gather further evidence.

Notes

Subpoenas

- *subpoena* - a legal order requiring the appearance of a person and/or the presentation of documents to a court or administrative body.
- *subpoena ad testificandum* - orders the appearance of a person at a trial or other investigative proceeding to give testimony.
- *subpoena duces tecum* - a written command to bring records, documents, or other evidence described in the subpoena to a trial or other investigative proceeding.

Kinds of Evidence

- Direct Evidence
- Demonstrative Evidence
- Documentary Evidence
- Examination of Witnesses
- Expert Witness Necessary

Defense Against Recovery

- Assumption of a Risk
- Comparative Negligence
- Contributory Negligence
- Good Samaritan Laws
- Ignorance of Fact and Unintentional Wrongs
- Statute of Limitations
- Sovereign Immunity

Chapter 7: Government, Ethics, & the Law

Notes

Chapter 7
Government, Ethics, &
the Law

Learning Objectives

- Describe meaning & sources of public policy.
- Describe important laws designed to protect individual's rights.
- Understand concept of "Political Malpractice."

Public Outcry

- Unethical conduct
  - moral decline
  - decaying value systems
- Questionable political decisions
- Numbers cooking money grabbing executives

Notes

Laws Influence Ethical Principles
Protecting Individual Rights – I

- XIV Amendment to the U.S. Constitution
- Sherman Antitrust Act
- Civil Rights Act
- Privacy Act
- Emergency Medical Treatment & Active Labor Act
- Health Care Quality Improvement Act

Laws Influence Ethical Principles
Protecting Individual Rights – II

- Agency for Healthcare Research & Quality
- Ethics in Patient Referral Act
- Patient Self-Determination Act
- Uniform Controlled Substances Act
- Federal Food, Drug & Cosmetic Act

Public Policy
A Principle of Law

Public policy: principle of law which holds no one can lawfully do that which tends to be injurious to public

Sources of Public Policy

- Legislation
- Administrative rules, regulations or decisions
- Judicial decisions
- Professional code of ethics may contain an expression of public policy

XIV Amendment to the U.S. Constitution – 1868

States
- cannot deny any person equal protection of law.
- shall not make or enforce any law which shall abridge privileges or immunities of citizens.
- shall not deprive any person of life, liberty, or property, without due process of law.
- shall not deny any person equal protection of laws.

Civil Rights Act – 1964

- Racial discrimination prohibited
- HHS program discrimination prohibited

Notes

Sherman Anti-Trust Act - 1890

- Contracts in restraint of trade illegal
- Areas of concern for health care
  - reduced market competition
  - price fixing
  - preferred provider arrangements
  - exclusive contracts

Privacy Act – 1974

- Safeguard individual privacy
- Provide individuals access to records
- Establish Privacy Protection Safety Commission

Emergency Medical Treatment & Active Labor Act – 1986

- Hospital Emergency Departments
  - required to provide appropriate medical screening exam
  - forbidden to "dump" patients from one emergency department to another.

Text Case: EMTALA Violated

- In *Burditt v. U.S. Department of Health & Human Services*, EMTALA was violated by a physician when he ordered a woman with dangerously high blood pressure (210/130) & in active labor with ruptured membranes transferred from the emergency department of one hospital to another hospital 170 miles away.

In *Burditt*

- What are the main issues in this case?
- What ethical theories, principles & values are of concern? Describe them.

Health Care Quality Improvement Act 1986

- Provide professional review bodies limited immunity from damages.
- Need to improve quality of medical care
  - Ability of incompetent physicians to move from State to State without disclosure of incompetence.
- Facilitate exchange of information among professionals conducting peer review.
- Protect physicians improperly subjected to disciplinary action.

Notes

Agency for Healthcare Research & Quality

- Improve quality of health care
- Reduce costs
- Broaden access to essential services

Ethics in Patient Referral Act - 1989

- Prohibits physicians who have ownership interest or compensation arrangements with clinical lab from referring Medicare patients to that lab
- Requires Medicare providers to report names & provider numbers of all physicians or their immediate relatives with ownership interests in a provider entity

Patient Self-Determination Act– 1990

- Right to be informed of rights.
- Right to execute advance directives.
- Right to accept or refuse medical care.
- States required to provide description of state laws regarding advance directives to providers.
- Providers ensure written policies & procedures regarding advance directives are established.

HIPAA – 1996

- Protect

  - Privacy of patient information
  - Confidentiality of patient information
  - Security of patient information

- Applicable to all health information in formats

Sarbanes-Oxley Act of 2002 - I

The Sarbanes-Oxley Act was signed into law by President Bush on July 30, 2002 in response to the Enron debacle & high profile cases of corporate mismanagement. The new corporate responsibility law hit health care in March 2003 when the SEC charged HealthSouth Corporation (and its CEO & former executives) with numerous violations of the new law.

Sarbanes-Oxley Act of 2002 – II
Promoting Due Diligence

- SOX is not about regulation; its about self-regulation.
- Selecting a leader with morals & core values.
- Examining incentives.
- Monitoring the organization's culture.
- Build a strong knowledgeable governing body.
- Searching for conflicts of interest.
- Focusing attention on the right things.
- Having courage to speak out.

Notes

Sarbanes-Oxley Act of 2002 – III
Know your Moral Values

- Be willing to stand up for them
- Be prepared to pay the cost

"the tragedy of society is not the noisiness of the so-called bad people, but the appalling silence of the so-called good people."

- Martin Luther King, Jr.

Sarbanes-Oxley Act of 2002 – IV
The "System"

Do not think lightly of evil, saying, "It will not come to me." By the constant fall of water drops in a pitcher, a pitcher is filled, accumulating evil little by little, becomes full of evil.

Buddha, Dhammapada verse 121

HealthSouth: First Test
Sarbanes-Oxley Act - I

CEO Scrushy's trial on corporate fraud charges opened with a prosecutor telling jurors Schrushy was the driving force behind a conspiracy to overstate earnings by about $2.7 billion. With underlings generating bogus financial statements to make it appear HealthSouth Corp. was meeting Wall Street forecasts from 1996 through 2002, a prosecutor argued, Scrushy sold about $150 million worth of his own HealthSouth stock & spent more than $200 million on a lavish lifestyle.

HealthSouth: First Test for Sarbanes-Oxley Act - II

The case is significant because it marks the first test of the 2002 Sarbanes-Oxley Act, which requires top executives of public corporations to vouch for the financial reports of their companies. The former CEO challenged the new corporate fraud law in November last year, but U.S. District Judge Karon O. Bowdre rejected the challenge.

Verdicts In

- June 29, 2006
- Former HealthSouth CEO Richard Scrushy was found guilty of all of the bribery, conspiracy and mail fraud counts brought against him.

HealthSouth: First Test for Sarbanes-Oxley Act - III

- Ethical Issues
  - Trustworthiness
    - Refer to Chapter 1
- Legal Issues
  - Fraud
    - Refer to Chapter 6
    - Also, consider the Sarbanes-Oxley Act
    - Discuss the potential outcome/s of this case.
    - Discuss the likely affect on health care organizations.

Notes

Chapter 8
Organizational Ethics
& the Law

Learning Objectives

- Understand ethical & legal risks for organizations.
- Describe corporate structure.
- Identify responsibilities of organizations.

Introduction - I

- Introduces ethical responsibilities & legal risks of organizations.
- Describe an organization's code of ethics which:
  - build trust.
  - increase awareness of ethical issues.
  - guide decision-making.
  - encourage staff to seek advice & report misconduct.

Notes

Introduction - II

- develop & maintain an environment that fosters high ethical & legal standards.
- provide quality care.
- treat patients with honesty, dignity, respect, & courtesy.

Organizational Structure

- Sole proprietorships
- Partnerships
- Corporations

Corporate Authority

- Described under the laws in which a corporation is chartered.

- Described in a corporation's articles of incorporation.

Kinds of Authority

- Express Corporate Authority

- Implied Corporate Authority

- Ultra Vires Acts

Respondeat Superior

- A legal doctrine holding employers liable for wrongful acts of their employees.
- Doctrine also referred to as *vicarious liability.*

Elements Needed to impute Liability to Employer

- Master–servant relationship must exist between employer & employee
- Wrongful act of employee must have occurred within scope of employee's employment

Notes

Notes

Independent Contractor

- Relationship established when principal has no right of control over manner in which agent's work is to be performed.

- Independent contractor responsible for his or her own negligent acts.

Corporate Negligence

- Corporation fails to perform duties it owes directly to a patient & patient is injured.

Benchmark *Darling Case*

The court in this case enunciated a "corporate negligence doctrine" under which hospitals have a duty to provide adequately trained medical & nursing staff.

Darling v. Charleston Community Memorial Hospital

Corporate Responsibility - I

- Appointment of CEO
- Medical Staff Appointments
- Allocation of Scarce Resources
- Compliance with Rules & Regulations
- Compliance with JCAHO Standards

Corporate Responsibility - II

- Provision of Timely Treatment
- Protect Patients from Professional's Incompetence
- Conflict-of-Interest
- Provision of a Safe Environment
- Prevent Health Care Fraud

Health Care Fraud – I

- Billing for services not performed.
- Falsifying records to perform unnecessary medical procedures.
- Misrepresenting procedures performed to obtain payment for non-covered services.

Notes

Health Care Fraud – II

- Upcoding—billing for a more costly service than the one actually performed.
- Unbundling—-billing each stage of a procedure as if it were a separate procedure.
- Accepting kickbacks for patient referrals.

Preventing Fraud – I

- Appoint compliance officer.
- Communicate organization's compliance program.
- Provide monitoring & auditing systems to detect criminal conduct.
- Publicize reporting system.

Preventing Fraud – II

- Take appropriate steps to respond to criminal conduct.
- Periodically review & update compliance program.
- Work with regulatory agencies detect, prevent & prosecute fraud.

Notes

Healthy Dose of Fraud

Agents say, recruiters bring "patients from across the nation to surgery centers in California where they give phoney or exaggerated symptoms & doctors perform unnecessary operations on them. Surgery centers send inflated claims for unnecessary procedures to the patients' insurance companies. When the insurers pay up, federal authorities say, the recruiters, surgery centers, & patients split proceeds.

Discuss the legal & ethical issues.

Management Decisions Collide with Professional Ethics

The principles of autonomy, beneficence, & justice & ability to practice what is right according to such principles often collide when organizations have to, for example, ration scarce resources. Such rationing may require managers to cut costs at the expense of quality.

Letter of Recommendation Case – 1

A former employer who knew that an employee had committed offensive sexual acts gave a letter of recommendation that vouched for him without reservation. The employee after being hired by the new employer injured the student-plaintiff.

Discuss the legal & ethical issues.

Notes

Legal Issues
Case – 1

- Liability may be imposed if the recommendation letter amounts to an affirmative misrepresentation presenting a
  - (1) *foreseeable,* &
  - (2) *substantial risk of physical harm* to a third person.

Legal Issues
Case – 1

- The defendants could foresee that, had they not recommended the employee, the employer would not have hired him.
- The defendants could foresee that the employer would read & rely on the defendant's letters of recommendation & that the employee after being hired by the new employer might molest or injure a student such as the plaintiff.

Randi W. v. Muroc Joint Unified School Dist., 14 Cal.4th 1066, 929 P.2d 582 (1997).

Ethical Issues
Case 1

- Do no harm
- Truthfulness

Letter of Recommendation
Case – 2

Mr. R's supervisor had received several reports alleging misconduct between Mr. R & some of the female residents in the Lee Allan nursing home. The supervisor was unable to verify them.

Mr. R applied for a supervisory position with Parke County Nursing Home. Parke County was sent a pre-printed reference form from Lee Allan. The form indicated Mr. R was eligible for re-hire. The form reflected that Mr. R performed his job adequately.

Letter of Recommendation
Case – 2 con't

The Parke County hired Mr. R in part on the basis of a favorable recommendation from Lee Alan. The claim here is that Mr. R assaulted a patient at Parke County. The plaintiff asserts that the former employer, Lee Allan, wrongly gave a favorable recommendation & thus should be liable for the injury.

Legal Issues

- Summary judgment was granted in favor of Lee Alan.
- The facts did not reflect that Lee Alan had any substantial information indicating that Mr. R had committed sexual misconduct with residents at Lee Alan.

Notes

Legal Issues

- Recommendations should not be filled with rumors & innuendo instead of facts. Without substantial evidence, employers would subject themselves to possible defamation litigation.
- Declaring employers liable for negligence in providing employment references will lead to employer reluctance to provide any information.
  Passmore v. Multi-Management Svcs., Inc., 810 N.E.2d 1022 (Ind. 2004).

Ethical Issues

- Beneficence
- Justice
- Fairness

Surgical Site Infection

OR staff observe a 10 inch by 2 inch tear in a surgical table mattress. It is 2:00 PM & the room has been prepared for Mrs. Smith's surgery. A surgical sheet is placed on the table. The sheet is worn & has several tears in it. Mrs. Smith is placed on the surgical table. [Note: Prior to Mrs. Smith's surgery, a bowel resection was performed on the same table.].
Discuss the legal & ethical concerns.

Legal Issues

- Legal Issues
  - Negligence?
  - Consider the hospital's responsibility
  - Torn mattress is a known infection control concern
    - Due to body fluid seepage into the mattress
    - Recurrent use of the mattress by various patient

Ethical Issues

- Ethical Issues
  - Nonmaleficience (first, do no harm)
    - Refer to Chapter 1
  - Professional codes of ethics (see next slide)
    - Refer to Chapter 9

Ethical & Legal Issues

- Professional Ethics
  - OR staff recognized that the mattress should have been taken out of service but failed to do so. It is common knowledge that body fluids that can seep into a mattress pad & provide a breeding ground for infecticious diseases.
  - Describe how hospital policy should address this issue.

Some Push to Make Hospitals Disclose Rates of Infection

"As many as two million patients at U.S. hospitals may develop infections each year, the Centers of Disease Control estimates. It says these may lead to more than 90,000 deaths annually-more than the total from breast cancer or car crashes. Hospital-acquired infections add roughly $5 billion a year to the cost of patient care in the U.S."

The Wall Street Journal: 2/1/05

Defrauding the Government - I

The government filed an indictment against eleven individuals & four corporations. In the indictment, the government alleged a health care fraud scheme that involved several residential care facilities, thousands of claims. The government alleged that over at least five years fifteen defendants, in various conspiracies, defrauded the government by falsely certifying patients as homebound & submitting false claims to Medicare & Medicaid.

States v. Liveoak, 377 F.3d 859 (C.A. 8, Mo. 2004)

Defrauding the Government - II

Joinder of Medicare fraud was proper where the charges here were linked not only by common conspiracy members, but also by an overall scheme in which each conspiracy member participated to fraudulently charge the government for health care costs.

Defrauding the Government - III Legal & Ethical Issues

- Legal Issues
  - Fraud
    - Refer to Chapter 6 & 7
- Ethical Issues
  - Trustworthiness
    - Refer to Chapter 1

Sexual Abuse

Dentist performs sexual acts on a patient while under conscious sedation.

Discuss the legal & ethical issues.

Ethical & Legal Issues

- Legal Issues
  - Criminal (sexual abuse)
- Ethical Issues
  - Trust
    - Refer Chapter 1
  - Professional codes of ethics

Notes

The ED & the Tick - I

Mrs. Smith had an autoimmune disease. To complicate her life, she had a tick imbedded in her skin kicking its tiny legs in the middle of her back. It was Saturday night & nowhere to go but to the local hospital's emergency department. Upon entry to the emergency department there was a sign:

3 hour wait for triage
5 hour wait for a physician

The ED & the Tick - II

Mrs. Smith was told that she would have to wait.

Discuss the concerns do you have with this scenario.

Legal & Ethical Issues

- Legal Issues
  - 2 hour wait for triage – what is the concern for other patients who may be delayed and have a life threatening event (e.g., MI, CVA, abdominal aneurysm) occur while waiting for triage.
- Ethical Issues
  - Compassion

Administration of Wrong Medication

Mrs. Jones was administered the wrong medication. As a result, the patient suffers a serious reaction. The nurse executive instructs the staff nurse, "don't tell anyone."

Discuss the legal & ethical issues.

Legal & Ethical Issues

- Legal Issues
  - Negligence
- Ethical issues
  - Autonomy
  - Truthfulness
- Regulatory issues
  - Joint Commission standards require reporting of mistakes made during the care of a patient.

Passing the Buck - I

Mrs. Smith, an acutely ill patient in pain, arrives for a scheduled CT scan at a hospital outpatient center to rule out a stroke. The physician's order which had been faxed to the center did not specify if the scan was to be performed without contrast. The medical assistant said to Mrs. Smith, "You will have to have your physician rewrite your prescription before we can perform the exam."

Notes

Notes

Passing the Buck - II

Mrs. Smith was distressed. The medical assistant then said, "He can fax it to us!" The medical assistant, pointing to a phone said, "There is a phone over there. The fax number is on the wall." Mr. Smith said he would make the call.

Discuss the legal & ethical issues.

Legal & Ethical Issues

- Legal Issues
  - Potential negligence issues?
    - Subjecting the patient to unnecessary stress could aggravate her medical problems.
- Ethical Issues
  - Beneficence (to do good)
    - Refer Chapter 1
  - Professional codes of ethics.
  - Compassion?

Failure to Disclose Financial Incentives

HMO failed to disclose financial incentive system it provided to its physicians to discourage referrals to specialists.

Discuss the legal & ethical issues.

Chapter 9: Health Care Professionals

Notes

Chapter 9
Health Care Professionals

Learning Objectives

- Understand how ethics & the law impact on health care professionals.
- Recognize similarities in various professional codes of ethics.
- Understand how ethical & legal issues described in any single case have applicability to health professions.

Introduction - I

- Codes of ethics demand a high level of integrity, honesty & responsibility.
- Codes of ethics developed to provide guidance to those faced with ethical dilemmas.
- Codes of ethics created in response to actual or anticipated ethical conflicts.

Introduction - II

- Codes of ethics vary depending on risks associated with a particular profession, for example
  - Ethical codes for psychologists define relationships with clients in greater depth due to personal one to one relationships.
  - Lab technicians & technologists have little or no direct contact with patients but can have a significant impact on their care. Lab technologists in their code of ethics "pledge accuracy & reliability in performance of tests."

Chiropractor

A chiropractor engaged in a conspiracy to manufacture & distribute a misbranded substance with the intent to defraud & mislead.

Chiropractor
Poor Judgment & Immoral Conduct

Nebraska law holds that a license to practice a health care profession may be revoked when licensee is guilty of immoral conduct. Patients rely upon chiropractor's honesty, integrity, sound professional judgment & compliance with applicable governmental regulations.

Poor Judgment & Immoral Conduct

- Did the chiropractor violate his professional code of ethics? Explain your answer.
- Describe ways in which an individual's personal life can have an impact on his or her professional career.

Dental Hygienist
Administration of Nitrous Oxide

A hearing panel found the dental hygienist guilty of administering nitrous oxide without being properly licensed. In addition, the hearing panel found that the hygienist had failed to accurately record in the patient's chart that she had administered nitrous oxide.

Administration of Nitrous Oxide

1. Describe how the core values of a dental ow both ethical & legal issues are intertwined in this case.
2. Describe how the core values of a dental hygienist were violated in this case.

Notes

Notes

Emergency Department
Case Reviews

- *Wrong Record Reviewed–Grave & Fatal Mistake*
- *What Common Sense Made Evident*
- *Failure to Respond*
- *Timely Response–May Require a Phone Call*
- *Emergency Rooms Vital to Public Safety*

Laboratory Technician
Code of Ethics

I. Duty to the Patient
II. Duty to Colleagues & the Profession
III. Duty to Society

Reporting False Lab Reports

Laboratory technologists, aware that testing of several hundred patients for HIV were incorrect, reported the inaccurate results as accurate. Ten percent of the patients were told that they were HIV positive. Follow-up testing revealed only one HIV positive patient.

Discuss the legal & ethical issues.

Testing Manipulated

1. Describe a laboratory technician's professional responsibility to report accurate laboratory tests.

2. Should a laboratory technician report less than accurate laboratory reports if required to do so by his or her supervisor? Explain your answer.

Legal & Ethical Issues

- Legal Issues
  - Fraud
    - Refer to Chapter 6
- Ethical Issues
  - Nonmaleficience (first, do no harm)
    - Refer to Chapter 1
  - Truthfulness
    - Refer to Chapter 1
  - Professional Codes of ethics
    - Refer to Chapter 9

Medical Assistant Code of Ethics

- Render service with full respect for the dignity of humanity.
- Respect confidential information.
- Uphold the honor & high principles of the profession.
- Seek to continually improve knowledge & skills of medical assistants.

Medical Records
Code of Ethics

1. Place service before material gain.

2. Preserve & protect the medical records.

4. Refuse to participate in or conceal unethical practices or procedures.

6. Preserve the confidential nature of professional determinations made by the staff committees.

9. Strive to advance knowledge & practice of medical record administration . . . contribute to the best possible medical care.

Nursing
Negligent Acts- I

- Nurse Assessments & Diagnosis
- Ambiguous Medication Order
- Wrong Dosage of a Medication
- Medicating the Wrong Patient
- Failure to Note Order Change

Nursing
Negligent Acts- II

- Failure to Follow Instructions
- Failure To Report Physician Negligence
- Failure to Question Patient Discharge
- Patient's Changing Condition

Pharmacist
Expanding Role

- Duty to Monitor Patient's Medications
- Warning Patients about Potential for Overdose
- Refusal to Honor a Questionable Prescription

Physical Therapist
Interpreting Physician's Orders

Physical Therapists' Code of Ethics, Principle 3.4 states that "any alteration of a program or extension of services beyond the program should be undertaken in consultation with the referring practitioner." Because resistive exercises were not set forth in the original prescription, Boulet stated that consultation with the physician was necessary before the Plaintiff could be advanced to that level.

Psychologists: Code of Ethics

10.07 Therapy With Former Sexual Partners
Psychologists do not accept as therapy clients/patients persons with whom they have engaged in sexual intimacies.

- **10.08 Sexual Intimacies With Former Therapy Clients/Patients**

(a) Psychologists do not engage in sexual intimacies with former clients/patients for at least two years after cessation or termination of therapy.

(b) Psychologists do not engage in sexual intimacies with former clients/patients even after a two-year interval except in the most unusual circumstance

Notes

Notes

Psychologist
Improprieties with clients

The Board of Psychologist Examiners revoked a psychologist's license for sexual improprieties. The psychologist argued that therapy had terminated before the sexual relationships began.

What did the court of Appeals decide? Why?

Psychologist
Improprieties with clients

The court of appeals held that evidence supported the board's conclusion that the psychologist had violated an ethical standard in caring for her patients.

Helpful Advice for Caregivers

- Abide by professional code of ethics.
- Do not criticize one's professional skills.
- Maintain complete & adequate medical records.
- Provide each patient with medical care comparable with national standards.
- Inform the patient of the risks, benefits & alternatives to proposed procedures.

Helpful Advice, cont.

- Participate in continuing education programs.
- Keep patient information confidential.
- Be a good listener & allow each patient sufficient time to express fears & anxieties.
- Closely monitor each patient's response to treatment.
- Provide education & teaching to patients.

Notes

Notes

_____
_____
_____
_____
_____
_____
_____
_____
_____
_____
_____
_____
_____
_____
_____
_____
_____
_____
_____
_____
_____
_____
_____
_____
_____
_____
_____
_____
_____
_____
_____
_____
_____
_____
_____
_____
_____
_____

Chapter 10
Physicians Ethical & Legal Issues

Learning Objectives

- Understand how ethics & law impact on physicians.
- Identify the variety & complexity of patient care issues that physicians face.
- Describe how practicing one's professional code of ethics can assist in resolving patient care issues.

Credentialing Process

- Hospital's Duty to Ensure Competency
- Physician Supervision & Monitoring

Notes

Disruptive Physicians

- Disruptive physicians have negative impact on staff & affect quality of care.
- Ability to work with others reasonably related to ensuring patient welfare.
- Lack of ability to work with others sufficient to support denial of privileges.

Abandonment

- Unilateral termination of physician–patient relationship
  - by the physician without notice to the patient.
- *Abandonment & the Hippocratic Oath*
  - Physician must notify patient if he is withdrawing from case
  - Hippocratic oath provides"
    - The regimen I adopt shall be for the benefit of my patients . . . not for their hurt . . . "

Alternative Procedures

- An adverse result following treatment is not in & of itself evidence of negligence
- Reasonable for two physicians to have differing opinions on the preferred method of treatment

Confidential Communications

- Physicians ethically bound to maintain patient confidences.

- Obligation applies to all professionals.

Falsification of Records

- Intentional falsification, or destruction of medical records.
  - to avoid liability for one's medical negligence.
  - generally sufficient to show actual malice.
- Tampering with records shatters one's credibility.
- Altered records can create presumption of negligence.

Emergency Department Call

- Physicians on emergency call are expected to respond to requests for assistance.
- Failure to respond is grounds for negligence should a patient suffer injury.

Notes

Emergency Department Care – I

Mr. Doe arrived in the ED at 12:00 AM complaining to the desk clerk of right face & arm numbness that had persisted since the day before. The clerk asked Mr. Doe to have a seat in the waiting area and that a triage nurse would be with him shortly. At 12:31 AM, Mr. Doe was taken to a triage room. Mr. Doe's vital signs were taken. His blood pressure was 190 over 119. After being triaged Mr. Doe's was asked to have a seat in the waiting area until he was called for treatment.

Emergency Department Care – II

At 1:09 AM, Mr. Doe was taken to a treatment room. At 1:40 AM, the ED physician ordered blood work and a CT scan. At 2:30 AM, Mr. Doe had his CT scan. At 3:10 AM, the nurse conducted a reassessment and noted that the patient's "speech was slightly slurred" with his mouth slightly off center. At 3:15 AM, Mr. Doe's CT results indicated suspicion for small infarcts.

Emergency Department Care – III

The treating physician was interviewed as to the patient's presenting symptoms (e.g., right sided numbness in face and arms), recorded vital signs (e.g., 190/119), and timeliness of care. The physician claimed that he was not concerned about the any delay in the patient's treatment due to the patient's symptoms or vital signs.

Emergency Department Care – IV

The nurse stated that there was no stroke protocol for use of TPA. The physician stated there were very few strokes in his community and that the jury was still out on the value of TPA in treating ischemic strokes.

How the Courts View
Poorly Conducted H&Ps – I

JD felt a severe headache. Paramedics took JD's history, which included hypertension. His blood pressure was high, ranging from 200/120 to 170/130. At the hospital, JD's vital signs were reassessed. His blood pressure was recorded at 170/130. Dr. M examined JD. Dr. M sent JD for x-rays. JD was diagnosed with a pinched nerve. Dr. M told JD he was being discharged with a muscle relaxant & an anti-inflammatory painkiller. Dr. M did not know JD's blood pressure when he treated him & did not review the ambulance records or the ER form.

How the Courts View
Poorly Conducted H&Ps – II

The next morning, JD was found unconscious on the floor. An ambulance crew responded & took JD's blood pressure four times between 7:16 and 7:50 a.m. The readings were extremely high (e.g. 220/120). At the hospital, a neurosurgeon diagnosed a hemorrhagic stroke. Excess fluid in JD's brain caused JD to lapse into a coma. The neurosurgeon believed that had he been called, he would have stopped bleeding by the time JD arrived at the emergency room the first day.

Notes

How the Courts View Poorly Conducted H&Ps – III

Dr. M was determined to have been "grossly negligent" because he " assessed, treated and discharged JD without knowing his blood pressure" & because he "did not actively seek out information about the blood pressure & medical history which might have led him to the correct diagnosis." Dr. M's failure to ascertain & assess information about a patient in order to adequately prepare a patient history fell below the standard of care for an ED physician & constituted gross negligence.

Moheet v. State Board of Registration for the Healing Arts, No. WD63543 (Mo. Ct. App. 2004).

Informed Consent

- Physician's have a duty to
  - Disclose known & risks, benefits & alternatives. to proposed treatment
  - Advise patients of treatment alternatives
  - Provide the necessary medical facts
- Patient's role
  - Make a treatment decisions based on understanding the risks & benefits of alternative treatments

Informed Consent
Surgical Options not Discussed

A lumpectomy has the same survival rate as a mastectomy. The surgeon performs a total mastectomy & does not discuss other options with Mrs. Smith.

Discuss the legal & ethical issues.

Notes

Legal & Ethical Issues

- Legal
  - Informed consent
    - Refer to Chapter 12
- Ethical
  - Truthfulness
    - Refer to Chapter 1

Failure to Read Nursing Notes

A surgeon breached his duty of care owed to the patient by failing to read the nurse's notes. Testimony convinced the court that the surgeon chose not to review the nurses' observations. The surgeon's failure to review nursing notes exacerbated an already critical condition & *deprived the patient of a chance of survival.*

Failure to Seek Consultation

If preferred treatment is outside a physician's field of expertise, it is his or her duty to advise the patient.

Inadequate History & Physical

A hospital's rules required a history & physical to be written within 24 hours of admission. No history had been completed. A jury might reasonably infer that if a history had been taken promptly, it might have helped in diagnosing the patient's condition.

Documentation Issues

Hospital policy require that a history & physical examinations be completed prior to patients undergoing surgery.

Smith's attending physician drew a diagonal line from the top right to the bottom left of the history & physical form, indicating that patient had no history of disease. The nurse documented on the admission that the patient had a history of trans-ischemic attacks, diabetes, & hypothyroidism.

Documentation Discussion

- What are the potential legal issues of concern?
- Discuss the ethical issues & principles violated in this case.

Unremarkable H&P

Mrs. Smith was admitted to the hospital with signs of an impending stroke. Her attending physician recorded in her history and physical examination that the family history was "unremarkable." The patient's mother actually died of a stroke and the father died of an MI.

Incomplete H&P – I

Dr. Dee is required, according to medical staff policy, to conduct a history & physical examination (h&p) on all patients admitted to the hospital. Dr. Dee admitted Mrs. Smith to remove her gallbladder. The required h&p form had a diagonal line drawn through the h&p, which included patient & family history.

Incomplete H&P - II

Upon questioning the physician as to the meaning of the diagonal line, Dr. Dee responded, "It should be obvious. There is no significant patient or family history." Review of the nursing assessment indicated that the patient was diabetic & had high blood pressure.

Discuss the legal & ethical issues.

Notes

Legal & Ethical Issues

- Legal Issues
  - Falsification of records?
  - Malpractice concerns?

- Ethical Issues
  - Falsification of records?
  - Truth telling
    - Refer to Chapter 1

Infection Control

- *Nosocomial Infection*: hospital acquired infections, are a leading cause of injury & unnecessary deaths.
- Such infections have been linked to unsanitary conditions in the environment & poor practices (e.g. hand-washing technique).
- Centers for Disease Control & Prevention estimates nearly two million patients annually get a nosocomial infection.

Medication Errors

- Thousands of brand & generic drugs in use.
- Med errors a leading cause of patient injuries.
- Negligent administration of medications often due to
  - wrong medication, wrong patient, wrong dose, wrong route, & wrong site.

Misdiagnosis

- Diagnosis is medical art - not exact science
- Misdiagnosis may involve diagnosis & treatment of
  - a disease different from that which patient actually suffers
  - a disease the patient does not have
  - symptoms but not the underlying disease
    - delayed diagnosis often occurs in autoimmune diseases: MS, Lupus, Systemic Scleroderma

Misdiagnosis
Heart Attacks Undiagnosed

"one in 50 heart attack victims are mistakenly sent home by emergency room doctors . . . . Connie Gustafson, who won her own battle with breast cancer, says her husband's fight to survive reminds her 'how vigilant you have to be in taking care of yourself in hospitals. The system is very precarious, and it is easy for mistakes to be made.'"

USA TODAY, October 25, 2006

Failure to Attend Delivery

The plaintiff in *Lucchesi v. Stimmell* brought an action against a physician for intentional infliction of emotional distress, claiming the physician failed to be present during unsuccessful attempts to deliver her premature fetus & that he failed to disclose to her that the fetus was decapitated during attempts to achieve delivery.

Discuss the legal & ethical issues.

Notes

Legal Issues

The judge instructed the jury that it could conclude that the physician had been guilty of extreme & outrageous conduct for staying at home & leaving the delivery in the hands of a first-year intern & a third-year resident, neither were experienced in breech births.

Ethical Issues

- Professional code of ethics.
- Conscientiousness

Duty to Warn

A patient allegedly killed a 3rd party after revealing his homicidal plans to his therapist. The therapist made no effort to inform the victim. The Court held that when a therapist determines or reasonably should determine a patient poses a serious danger to others, there is a duty to exercise reasonable care to protect foreseeable victims & warn them of impending danger.

Discuss the legal & ethical issues.

Exceptions to Duty to Warn

No duty on part of hospital or treating psychiatrists in *Sharpe v. So. Carolina Dept. of Mental Health* to warn general public of potential danger that might result from a psychiatric patient's release from state hospital. There was no identifiable threat to decedent who was shot by the patient. There was nothing in the record that indicated the former patient & decedent had known each other prior to the patient's release.

Wrong Site Surgery

Physician did not review patient's imaging scans prior to surgery. He did not have the films in the OR during surgery. The physician did not observe gross abnormalities in the left kidney & was unable to palpate any masses. Nonetheless, he removed the left kidney. The physician discharged the patient with a postoperative diagnosis of left renal mass, failing to note that he had in fact removed a tumor-free kidney.

Discuss the legal & ethical issues.

Mastectomy without Biopsy

Dr. Surge found a lump in Mrs. Smith's breast. He is sure the lump is cancer & admits Mrs. Smith to Community Hospital, a remote hospital in North Dakota, to undergo a mastectomy. The hospital has no pathologist. Dr. Surge performs the mastectomy without first performing a less invasive biopsy, as required by hospital policy.

Notes

Mastectomy without Biopsy, con't

As per hospital policy, the tissue removed was sent to a university hospital 300 miles away for microscopic review by a pathologist. Final diagnosis indicated that the tumor was benign.

Discuss the legal & ethical issues.

Legal & Ethical Issues

- Legal Issues
  - Malpractice by the surgeon
  - Negligence of the hospital
    - Refer Chapter 8

- Ethical Issues
  - Nonmaleficience
    - Refer to Chapter 1
  - Professional Codes of Ethics

A Gruff Physician - I

Dr. Gruff, an autoimmune disease disorder specialist, asked Mrs. Smith to lie on the exam table so that she could exam her. With Dr. Gruff standing beside her at the exam table, Mrs. Smith reaches for Dr. Gruff's hand to help ease herself down on the table. Dr. Gruff pulls her hand away saying, "You don't need my help."

A Gruff Physician - II

Mrs. Smith's spouse watches but says nothing. The exam involved Dr. Gruff pressing lightly on Mrs. Smith's abdomen in three places. Mrs. Smith asked, "Can you check my fingers. They are blue-black and one is infected." Dr. Gruff replied, "I don't know what you expect me to do." The patient raising from the table attempted to grasp Dr. Gruff's hand again for assistance. Gruff pulled away saying, "You got down! You can get up!"

A Gruff Physician - III

Mr. Smith upon arriving home decides, unbeknownst to his wife, to call Dr. Gruff regarding the cruel manner in which his wife was treated. Dr. Gruff said, "She doesn't have to come back!" Mr. Smith replied, "that is my wife's decision. I just wanted you to know how unprofessional I perceived your care was."

A Gruff Physician - IV

Mrs. Smith was contacted by a letter from Dr. Gruff telling Mrs. Smith that she could find a new physician.

Discuss the legal & ethical issues.

Notes

Legal & Ethical Issues

- Legal Issues
  - Abandonment? Probably not - no injury
  - Caveat – Dr. Gruff should be considered because of the emotional distress caused the patient.
- Ethical Issues
  - Beneficence
    - Refer to Chapter 1
  - Professional codes of ethics

Psychiatrist Dates Patient

After discontinuing psychoanalysis for a year, Ms. Smith's psychiatrist decides to date Ms. Smith.

Discuss the legal & ethical issues.

Legal & Ethical Issues

- Legal Issues
  - Difficult to establish in such cases
- Ethical Issues
  - Trust
    - Refer to Chapter 1
  - Professional codes of ethics
    - Refer to Chapter 9

Notes

Chapter 11
Employee Rights &
Responsibilities

Employee Rights

- Clear job expectations.
- Be consulted about decisions which affect you.
- Refuse unreasonable requests.
- Know how your performance is measured.
- Equal pay for equal work.
- Fair treatment.
- Safe Environment.
- Freedom from discrimination.

Right to Equal Pay for Equal Work
Equal Pay Act

- Prohibits wage disparities based on sex.
- Prohibits discrimination in payment of wages for women & men performing substantially equal work in same establishment.
- Wages may be unequal as long as they are based on factors other than sex, for example:
  - formalized seniority system.
  - system that objectively measures earnings by quantity or quality of production.

Notes

Right to Refuse to Participate in Care

- Participation in elective abortions
- Disconnecting a respirator

Right to Question Patient's Care

- Public policy clearly mandates an *obligation to serve the best interests of patients.*
- Persistence to get the proper treatment for the patient is an absolute duty.

Free from Sexual Harassment

- Employees have a right to be free from sexual harassment
- Sexual harassment includes:
    - request for a sexual favour/s.
    - sexual advances, condition employment.
    - unreasonably interfering with employee's work.
    - creating intimidating or offensive working environment.

Change Your Physician - I

Physician failed to return the nurse's calls. Because of the patient's deteriorating condition, the family contacted the nurse. After the nurse advised the patient's family as to her concerns, a member of the patient's family asked her what they should do. The nurse advised that she would reconsider their "choice of physicians." The nurse was terminated because she had advised the patient's family to consider changing physicians.

Discuss what action the hospital might take?

Change Your Physician - II

- What should the jury do? Discuss your answer.
- Discuss the legal issues in this case.
- Discuss the ethical issues in this case.
- What was the court's decision?

Change Your Physician - III

The North Carolina Court of Appeals held that the nurse stated a claim for wrongful discharge in violation of public policy. The nurse's termination for fulfilling her responsibilities as a practicing nurse violated state public policy & was a factual question for jury determination.

Notes

Notes

Fair Treatment in Employment

An "at will" prerogative without limits could be suffered only in an anarchy & there not for long, it certainly cannot be suffered in a society such as ours without weakening the bond of counter balancing rights & obligations that holds such societies together.

Sides v. Duke

Employment At-Will Doctrine

Provides that employment is at the will of either the employer or the employee

Employment may be Terminated

- by the employer or the employee at any time for any or no reason, unless there is a contract in place that specifies the terms & duration of employment.
  - public policy considerations
  - implied covenant of good faith & fair dealing

Public Policy Exceptions & Employee Rights

- Public policy exception to the employment-at-will doctrine provides that employees may not be terminated for reasons contrary to public policy

- Public policy originates with legislative enactments that prohibit discharge of employees

Public Policy Prohibiting Discharge

- Disability
- Age
- Race
- Creed
- Color
- Religion
- Sex
- National Origin
- Pregnancy
- Filing of safety violation complaints with OSHA

Retaliatory Discharge

- Tendency for those in power to abuse that power through threats, abuse, intimidation, & retaliatory discharge.
- Employees who become the targets of a vindictive supervisor often have difficulty in proving a bad-faith motive.
- Some states (e.g., Connecticut, Maine, Michigan, & Montana) have enacted legislation that protects employees from terminations found to be arbitrary & capricious.

Notes

Employee Responsibilities - I

- Be Dependable
- Be a Patient Advocate
- Be Compassionate
- Honor Patient Wishes
- Maintain Confidentiality
- Adhere to Safe Practices
  - *Hand washing*

Employee Responsibilities - II

- Exercise Judgment
- Adhere to Professional Standards
- Maintain Professional Relationships
  - *Nurse's Relationship with Patient*
  - *Physician's Inappropriate House Call*
  - *Avoid Sexual Misconduct*

Employee Responsibilities - III

- Report Unethical Behavior
- Protect Patients from Harm
- Report Patient Abuse
- Whistle-Blowing and Unethical Conduct

Caregivers Right

The nurse in the operating suite refuses to participate in an elective abortion.

Discuss how an organization might fairly address this dilemma.

Legal & Ethical Issues

- Legal Issues
  - Employee's right to religious freedom
  - Organization's responsibility to provide care

- Ethical Issues
  - Nonmaleficience (first, to do no harm)
    - Refer to Chapter 1
  - Professional codes of ethics
    - Refer to Chapter 9

Notes

Notes

Chapter 12
Patient Consent

Learning Objectives

- Describe a patient's right to self-determination.
- Describe various aspects of informed consent:
  - Assessing capacity to consent
  - Adequacy of consent
  - Proof of consent
  - Authorization for consent
  - Implied consent
  - Right to refuse to consent
  - Statutory consent

Consent

The voluntary agreement by a person who possesses sufficient mental capacity to make an intelligent choice to allow something proposed by another to be performed.

Notes

Consent: Express or Implied

- *Express consent*: a verbal or written agreement authorizing treatment.
- *Implied consent*: a presumption that consent has been authorized based on the nature of the patient's condition.
  - Comatosed state due to car accident

Informed Consent

- Legal concept that provides that a patient has a right to know potential risks, benefits, & alternatives of a proposed treatment.
- Requires that a patient have a full understanding of that to which he or she has consented.
- Any glimmer of uncertainty as to a patient's desires in an emergency situation should be resolved in favor of preserving life.

Matter of Hughes

- Patients have an obligation to make medical preferences known
  - including course to follow, if life-threatening complications arise
- Protects patient's right to freedom of religion & self-determination

Decision-Making Capacity - I

- Clinical assessment of decision-making capacity should include the patient's ability to
- understand the risks, benefits, & alternatives of a procedure.
  - evaluate the information provided by the physician.
  - voluntarily make decisions regarding his or her treatment plan without undue influence by family, friends, or medical personnel.

Decision-Making Capacity - II

- Before declaring an individual incapacitated, the attending physician must
  - determine with reasonable degree of medical certainty that the patient lacks capacity.
  - make a notation in the medical record describing the reason for incapacity.

Failure to Inform - I

A patient underwent a mastectomy only to learn that a less destructive alternative procedure was available in a region near her home. The procedure, a lumpectomy, has the same survival rate as a mastectomy. The patient claims the surgeon never informed her as to the alternative.

Notes

Failure to Inform - II

- Describe the ethical & legal issues for failing to discuss alternative treatments with a patient.
- Should a physician describe every possible alternative treatment procedure with his or her patient? Explain your answer.

Consent Forms Should Include

- nature of illness or injury
- procedure or treatment consented to
- purpose of proposed treatment
- risks & probable consequences of proposed treatment
- signatures of the patient, physician, & witnesses
- date the consent is signed

Who May Authorize Consent

- Competent Patients
- Spouse
- Guardian
- Parents of Minor

Consent for Minors

- Consent of minor can be ineffective
  - physician should secure consent of minor's parent if time allows.
- Treatment should not be delayed to detriment of child.
- Parental consent not necessary when minor emancipated.

Parents Refuse Transfusion for their Child - I

Parents refused to consent to care for their minor child based on religious convictions. The trial court appointed hospital as temporary guardian

In midst of emergency, District Court was confronted with task of balancing the competing interests of child, parents, hospital & State

District Court appointed hospital as temporary guardian. Supreme Court of Nevada affirmed order of District Court appointing Valley Hospital as temporary guardian

Parents Refuse Transfusion for their Child - II

- Discuss the legal implications of this case
  - e.g., states rights

- Discuss the ethical issues of this case
  - e.g., beneficence

Notes

Incompetent Patients

- The mentally incompetent cannot legally consent to treatment.

Right to Refuse Treatment

- Patients have a right to refuse treatment & be secure from any touching.
- A competent adult patient has right to decline any & all forms of medical intervention, including lifesaving or life-prolonging treatment.

Refusal to Consent can be

- Grounded on lack of confidence in the physician
- Due to fear of the procedure
- doubt as to the value of a procedure
- Based on mere whim.

State Rights

- preservation of life
- protection of third parties
- Prevention of suicide

Right to Refuse Treatment

In *In re Fetus Brown*, the State of Illinois asserted that its interest in the well-being of a viable fetus outweighed the patient's rights to refuse medical treatment. The state argued that a balancing test should be used to weigh state interests against patient rights. The appellate court held that it could not impose a legal obligation upon a pregnant woman to consent to an invasive medical procedure for the benefit of her viable fetus.

Justice Cardozo
Schloendorff v. Society of New York Hospital

Every human being of adult years & sound mind has a right to determine what shall be done with his own body . . . .

Notes

Florida District Court of Appeal

Health care providers must comply with wishes of a patient to refuse medical treatment unless ordered to do otherwise by a court. A health care provider cannot act on behalf of the state to assert state interests. When a health care provider, acting in good faith, follows the wishes of a competent and informed patient to refuse medical treatment, the health care provider is acting appropriately and cannot be subjected to civil or criminal liability.

Statutory Consent

- An emergency in most states eliminates the need for consent.
- When a patient is clinically unable to give consent to a lifesaving emergency treatment, the law implies consent.

Mother Refuses Treatment Spouse Agrees

- What would you do when a patient refuses a blood transfusion & the spouse agrees with her decision, knowing that a blood transfusion may be necessary to save her life?
- Should a hospital challenge a patient's refusal of lifesaving blood transfusions?

Complex Case

What do you do when the non-prominent personality of a patient with multiple personalities signs a consent form to undergo a major surgical procedure?

Ethics & the Law Intertwine

The individual with multiple personalities illustrates the complexities of ethical & legal issues facing caregivers.

Discuss how you would respond to the legal & ethical issues?

Parents Refuse Blood

The parents of a six year old child with multiple trauma refuse to consent for the administration of blood. The emergency department physician informs the parents that such refusal will most likely result in the death of the child.

Discuss the legal & ethical issues.

Legal & Ethical Issues

- Legal Issues
  - Parents rights
  - State interests
    - Refer to Chapter 12

- Ethical Issues
  - Autonomy
    - Child's rights
  - Beneficence (to do good)
  - Nonmaleficence (first, to do no harm)
    - Refer to Chapter 1

Blood Refusal: Competent Adult

Mrs. Smith, a mother of three refuses a blood transfusion which is considered necessary by a trauma team to save her life.

Discuss the legal & ethical issues.

Legal & Ethical Issues

- Legal Issues
  - Informed consent
    - » Refer to Chapter 12
- Ethical Issues
  - Autonomy (right to make own decisions)
  - Beneficence (to do good)
  - Nonmaleficience (first, to do no harm)
    - Impact on Caregivers
      - » Refer to Chapter 1
  - Professional codes of ethics
    - » Refer to Chapter 9

Blood Refusal: Spouse Disapproves

Mr. Smith refuses a blood transfusion necessary to save his life. Mrs. Smith wishes to override her husband's signed informed consent. The spouse is now in a comatose state.

Discuss the legal & ethical issues.

Ethical & Legal Issues

- Legal Issues
  - Informed consent
    - Refer to Chapter 12
- Ethical Issues
  - Autonomous rights of the patient
  - Beneficence (quality of being kind)
  - Nonmaleficience (first, do no harm)
    - Refer to Chapter 1

Chapter 13: Patient Abuse
Chapter

Notes

Chapter 13
Patient Abuse

Learning Objectives

- Understand the pervasiveness of patient abuse.
- Identify the signs of abuse.
- Describe the reporting requirements for abuse.

Introduction

Love and knowledge led upwards to the heavens, But always pity brought me back to earth; Cries of pain reverberated in my heart Of children in famine, of victims tortured
And of old people left helpless. I long to alleviate the evil, but I cannot,
And, I too suffer. This has been my life; I found it worth living.

Bertrand Russell, adapted

Patient Abuse

- Mistreatment of elderly patients is rampant.
- Facilities of refuge become institutions of misery & gloom.
- Who says, "I just can't wait to go to the nursing home/facility?"
- Nursing facilities should be places of hope not hopelessness.
- Need to change the paradigm.

Abuse can take many forms

- Physical
- Psychological
- Medical
- Financial

Elder Abuse – the Statistics

USA Today review between 2000-2002 - more than 5,300 assisted living facilities, found that what should be havens for the elderly may in reality be exposing them to deadly risks.

Seniors Fail to Report Abuse for Fear of:

- retaliation
- not being believed
- threats of being placed in a nursing facility
- physical & mental abuse

Signs of Abuse - I

- Unexplained or unexpected death.
- Development of pressure sores.
- Sedation used in place of adequate nursing staff.
- Occurrence of broken bones.
- Sudden & unexpected emotional outbursts.

Signs of Abuse - II

- Agitation
- Withdrawal
- Bruises
- Welts
- Discoloration

Notes

Signs of Abuse - III

- Burns
- Absence of hair
- Haemorrhaging below the scalp
- Dehydration &/or malnourishment without illness-related cause
- Hesitation to talk openly
- Implausible stories
- Unusual activity in bank accounts

The Hidden Camera

Gale wasn't prepared for the rough treatment & cruel taunts she says her ailing mother suffered at the nursing home. She cried as a nurse's aide chastised her mother for failing to straighten her arthritic-stricken legs & she watched in disbelief as an assistant jerked her mother off her rubber bed pad & pushed her into the bed's metal rails. All of these images were caught by a "granny cam"—a camera hidden in her mother's room.

Discuss the legal & ethical issues.

Documentation

- Document suspicions of abuse.
- Be thorough in documentation.
- Accurately document signs of suspected abuse.
- Be objective & clear when defining physical and physiological findings.

Neglect of Residents I
Text Case

- Residents exposed to unsanitary physical conditions.
- Grossly deprived of medical care.
- Conditions caused injury to physical & mental well-being.
- Fire hazards impeded safety
- Facility was not properly maintained (e.g., broken glass in patients' rooms).

Neglect of Residents II
Text Case

- Excessive hot water in faucets.
- Dried feces on public bathroom walls & grab bars.
- Insufficient towels & linens.
- Dead & live cockroaches & worms in the food preparation area.
- No soap available in the kitchen.

Neglect of Residents III
Text Case

- At one point only one bar of soap & one container of shampoo found in the entire facility.
- Dietary facilities unsanitary & inadequate to meet dietary needs of residents.
- Inadequate staffing patterns & supervision in the facility.
- Improper dosages of medications administered to residents.

Neglect of Residents IV
Legal Issues: Neglect

Defendant argued that he did not "create" unsafe conditions at facility. The court of appeals disagreed. The statute does not require that defendant create conditions at facility to sustain a conviction. Defendant was administrator of facility & responsible for conditions that existed.

Neglect of Residents IV
Ethical Issues

- Beneficence
- Compassion

Text Cases

- Abusive Search
- Forcible Administration of Medications
- Intimidation of Abusive Resident/Disciplinary Overkill
- Care Given Deceased Deficient

Child Abuse

- An abused child is generally defined as a person younger than 18 years of age whose parent or other person legally responsible for care:
  - inflicts physical injury.
  - allows, permits, or encourages a child to engage in unlawful conduct.

Reporting Abuse

- All states have enacted laws to protect abused children.
- Good faith reporting statutes
  - generally require mandatory reporting.
  - provide immunity for good-faith reporting.

Physical Indicators of Abuse

- Appear to be part of a pattern
  - Bruises
  - Burns
  - Broken bones
  - Withdrawal

Notes

Behavioral indicators of Abuse

- Diminished psychological or intellectual functioning.
- Failure to thrive.
- No control of aggression.
- Self-destructive impulses.
- Decreased ability to think & reason
- acting out, misbehavior, or habitual truancy.

Child Abuse
Nurse Fails to Report? - I

A 2 year old child had been airlifted from his foster home to a hospital. The flight crew reported to a hospital nurse that rescue personnel discovered dime size bruises under the child's eye & down his spine. The nurse did not document the bruises or notify the state's child abuse hotline. Dominic recovered after treatment & was released from the hospital on August 14, 2002. Four days later, on August 18, Dominic was returned to the hospital where he died of "abusive head trauma."

Nurse Fails to Report? - II

The nurse was criminally charged for failing to report the abuse & neglect under Mo. law. because the boy's mother said the bruises were the result of the boy leaning back in his booster seat.

State v. Brown, 140 S.W.3d 51 ((Mo.2004).

Nurse Fails to Report? - III

1. Describe the legal & ethical issues.
2. What additional questions should be answered before making a final decision as to the nurse's alleged neglect in reporting child abuse?

Nurse Fails to Report? - IV

1. Did the defendant nurse have information that the boy's condition had already been reported to the hot line?
2. Had other health care personnel, under a duty to report, already called the hot line?
3. Were the other personnel -- including health care professionals -- unaware that Dominic's condition triggered their duty to report?
4. Were the boy's injuries too subtle -- despite their graphic description here -- for health care professionals to discern that a hot line report was required?

Nurse Fails to Report? – V

- Legal Issues
  - failure to comply with state law
  - child abuse reporting statutes
  - failure to conduct a thorough nursing assessment
    - Refer to Chapter 9
- Ethical Issues
  - failure to adhere to ethical principles.
  - failure to comply with professional code of ethics
    - Refer to Chapter 9

Notes

Child Abuse
Physician Fails to Report? - I

Action was filed by Draper, as parent of Bryanna Draper, a three-month old infant who died on June 2, 2000, after being abused by her father. Plaintiff alleged that Bryanna had been admitted to the hospital in May 2000. X-rays showed numerous injuries. Defendant radiologists who read the x-rays failed to report injuries.

Physician Fails to Report? - II

Plaintiff alleged the defendant represented to law enforcement authorities that an x-ray taken on May 12 should have been read as abnormal, but that the abnormality was not of great concern, & inferred that it did not indicate abuse. Plaintiff alleged the defendant did not file an addendum to the report noting the presence of an abnormality until June 5, three days after Bryanna's death, & plaintiff concluded the defendant violated the applicable standard of care.

Draper v. Westerfield, No. E2003-02381-COA-R3-CV (Ct. App. Tenn. 2004)

Physician Fails to Report? - III

- Legal Issues
  - Failure to Comply with state law
    - Child abuse reporting statutes
  - Ethical Issues
  - Failure to adhere to ethical principle
    - Refer to Chapter 1
  - Failure to comply with professional code of ethics
    - Refer to Chapter 10

Chapter 14: Patient Rights and Responsibilities

Notes

_____

_____

_____

_____

_____

_____

_____

_____

_____

_____

_____

_____

_____

_____

_____

_____

_____

_____

_____

_____

_____

_____

_____

_____

_____

_____

_____

_____

_____

_____

_____

_____

_____

_____

_____

_____

_____

_____

_____

_____

_____

_____

_____

_____

Chapter 14
Patient Rights and
Responsibilities

Learning Objectives

- Describe & understand patient rights.
- Describe & understand patient responsibilities.

Help! I'm Wrestling with my Values

- Should I accept a blood transfusion if it will save my life?
- Should I refuse a blood transfusion and risk death because it is against my religious beliefs?
- Did I do a bad thing by refusing blood to save my life?
- Was I immoral to accept life over death or death over life?

Notes

_____

_____

_____

_____

_____

_____

_____

_____

_____

_____

_____

_____

_____

_____

_____

_____

_____

_____

_____

_____

_____

_____

_____

_____

_____

_____

_____

_____

_____

_____

_____

_____

_____

_____

_____

_____

_____

_____

_____

_____

_____

_____

_____

_____

_____

Patient Rights - I

- Right to Know Patient Rights
- Right to Explanation of Patient Rights
- Right to Participate in Care Decisions
- Right to Informed Consent

Patient Rights - II

- Right to Ask Questions
- Right "Not" to Know Treatment Options
- Right to Refuse Treatment
- Right to Execute Advance Directives
- Right to Designate a Decision Maker

Patient Rights - III

- Right to Privacy & Confidentiality
- Right to Know of Restrictions on Rights
- Right to Have Special Needs Addressed
- Right to Emergency Care
- Right to Discharge

Patient Rights - IV

- Right to Transfer
- Right to Access Medical records
- Right to Know of 3rd Party Care Relationships
- Right to Know the Caregivers

Patient Rights - V

- Right to Sensitive & Compassionate Care
- Right to a Timely Response to Care Needs
- Right to Pain Management

Spouse Requests Wife's Lab Results

Mrs. Smith had a pregnancy test. Mr. Smith called Mrs. Smith's physician & requested a copy of Mrs. Smith's test results.

Discuss the legal & ethical issues.

Notes

Legal & Ethical Issues

- Legal Issues

  – Right to privacy (e.g., HIPPA)
    » Refer to Chapter 7

- Ethical Issues
    » Refer to Chapter 14

Patient Responsibilities - I

- Ask questions.
- Discuss pain relief treatment with caregivers.
- Work with caregivers to develop pain control plan.
- Adhere to the pain control plan.
- Inform caregivers about prescriptions or over the counter medicines.

Patient Responsibilities - II

- Report pain to caregivers.
- Provide caregivers with information pain control methods that have worked well.
- Provide physician/s with complete health information.
- Follow physician's instructions for further care or tests.

Notes

Patient Responsibilities - III

- Report unexpected changes in condition to caregivers.
- Understand the plan of care.
- Follow the treatment plan recommended
  - Accept the consequences of not following the prescribed treatment plan.
- Follow organization's rules & regulations.

Patient Responsibilities - IV

- Be considerate of the rights of others
  - assist in control of noise, smoking, & visitors.
- Be respectful of the property of others.
- Recognize effect of life-style as it affects personal health.
- Keep appointments & be on time.

Patient Responsibilities – V
Speak-Up & Ask Questions

- Medications
- Diet
- Home exercise
- Infection control
  - ask caregivers if they washed their hands
- Fear Not
  - to ask for opinion/s
- Universal Protocol
  - Invasive procedures (e.g., surgery)
  - be sure staff accurately mark the correct site

Notes

_____
_____
_____
_____
_____
_____
_____
_____
_____
_____
_____
_____
_____
_____
_____
_____
_____
_____
_____
_____
_____
_____
_____
_____
_____
_____
_____
_____
_____
_____
_____
_____
_____
_____
_____
_____
_____
_____

Patient Responsibilities - VI

- Surrogate decision maker
  - advise caregivers who your decision maker will be in the event you become unable to make care decisions
- understand caregiver instructions
  - ask questions

Notes

Notes